FARM WORKSHOP

Farming Book Series

FARM
WORKSHOP

BRIAN BELL

FARMING PRESS LIMITED
WHARFEDALE ROAD, IPSWICH, SUFFOLK, ENGLAND

First published 1981

ISBN 0 85236 112 2

Printed and Bound by Robert Hartnoll Ltd., Bodmin

Contents

CHAPTER   PAGE

Introduction   **11**

1   The Farm Workshop   **13**
The site and building—stores—safety

2   Workshop Tools   **25**
HAND TOOLS: Spanners—screwdrivers—hammers—pliers and grips—punches—chisels—files—hacksaws—hand drills—tinsnips—bolt cutters—taps and dies—reamers—measuring tools—the micrometer—marking tools
POWER TOOLS: Drills — grinders — power hacksaws — shearing machines—extension cables
GENERAL WORKSHOP EQUIPMENT: Compressors—battery chargers — lifting tackle — vices — pullers — lubrication equipment — special tools

3   The Workshop Stores   **81**
Nuts and bolts—rivets—keys and pins—washers—gaskets and seals—other small items

4   Materials in the Farm Workshop   **100**
Metals: ferrous—steel—heat treatment of steel—identifying types of iron and steel—non-ferrous metals—other material

5   Soldering and Welding   **113**
Soldering—oxy-acetylene welding—oxy-acetylene cutting—electric-arc welding

6   Dealing with Corrosion   **141**
Cleaning equipment: wire brushes—abrasive sheets—cleaners and washers—rust prevention—painting—wood preservatives

7   Farm Plumbing   **153**
Tools—pipe bending—pipe dies—pipe fittings—plumbing with copper pipe—plumbing with plastic pipe—taps—ball valves—automatic drinkers—installing pipework—frost protection

8   Working with Metal   **173**
Riveting—forging—home-made tools—sheet metal work

CHAPTER   PAGE

9   General Repair Work   **182**

Seized nuts and bolts—broken studs—difficult studs, screws and pins—bearings and bushes—seals—sharpening—vee-belt drives—other types of belt—chain drives—overload devices—wiring a seven-pin trailer plug—tyres—electric motors

10   Tractor Repairs   **206**

Fuel economy—injectors—cooling—wheels and brakes—adding weight: water ballast—the clutch—setting valve tappets—misfiring—starting problems

Metrication Conversion Tables   **216**

Additional Reading   **217**

Index   **218**

Illustrations

Fig. No.   PAGE

 1. A typical diesel fuel storage system   18
 2. Spanners   27
 3. Socket spanners   28
 4. Spanner size   29
 5. Screwdrivers   30
 6. Screwdriver sharpening   31
 7. Hammers   33
 8. Pliers and grips   35
 9. Types of punch   37
10. Types of chisel   39
11. Chisel sharpening   40
12. Using chisels   41
13. Files—grades and cuts   43
14. Types of file   44
15. Filing technique   46
16. Using a hacksaw   49
17. Tinsnips   50
18. Sharpening and using tinsnips   50
19. Bolt cutters   51
20. Taps and dies   52
21. Reamers   56
22. Measuring tools   57
23. Micrometer   58
24. Reading a metric micrometer   59
25. Reading an imperial micrometer   60
26. Electric drills and attachments   62
27. Sharpening twist drills   65
28. Bench grinders   66
29. Portable grinders   69
30. Using a hydrometer   73
31. Metalwork vice   76
32. Fitting a vice to a bench   77
33. Hub puller   78
34. Lubrication equipment   79
35. Test micrometer readings   80

Fig. No. PAGE

36. Types of bolt 83
37. Bolt and screw heads 83
38. Types of nut 84
39. Dimensions of a thread 86
40. Locking devices for nuts and bolts 90
41. Types of rivet 91
42. Keys and pins 92
43. Removing a gib head key 93
44. Types of circlip 95
45. Fuel pipe unions 98
46. Tempering a cold chisel 104
47. Spark patterns of common ferrous metals 107
48. Oxy-acetylene welding set 117
49. Welding flames 119
50. Edge preparation for butt welding mild steel 120
51. Basic welding joints 121
52. Leftward welding technique 122
53. Rightward welding technique 123
54. Hard surfacing technique 124
55. Nozzle cleaning 124
56. Oxy-acetylene cutting blowpipe 125
57. Formation of an electric arc weld 128
58. Striking an arc 131
59. Effects of incorrect current settings 132
60. Fillet welding 134
61. Overhead and vertical welding 135
62. Hints on welding cast iron 137
63. Wire brushes 142
64. Pipe grips 154
65. Pipe cutters 155
66. Hole saw 156
67. Compression joint 160
68. Capillary joint 160
69. Common pipe fittings 161
70. Polythene pipe connector 163
71. Taps 164
72. Working parts of a tap 165
73. Stopcocks 165
74. Working parts of a stop tap 166
75. Ball valve 167
76. Automatic drinker 168
77. Pipe couplings 171
78. Stages of riveting 175

Fig. No.   PAGE
79. Some forging tools   177
80. Forging an eye   178
81. Working with sheet metal   179
82. Cutting through a seized nut   183
83. Working with bearings and seals   186
84. Removal of power shaft bearings   187
85. Vee-belt tension   190
86. Types of drive belt   192
87. Roller chains   195
88. Care of chain drives   196
89. Chain extractor   197
90. Measuring chain wear   197
91. Shortening a roller chain   198
92. Serrated face slip clutch   200
93. Friction plate slip clutch   200
94. Wiring a seven-pin plug   202
95. Diesel engine lift pump and sediment bowl   208
96. Removing an injector   209
97. Setting valve tappets   213

List of Tables

Table No.   PAGE

1. Dimensions of some typical large farm machines   15
2. Grades of file cut   42
3. Selection of hacksaw blades   48
4. Tapping drill sizes—BSW and BSF   54
5. Tapping drill sizes—UNC and UNF   54
6. Tapping drill sizes—metric   55
7. Tapping drill sizes—BS pipe   55
8. Lubricants for drilling and cutting metal   64
9. Specific gravity of battery electrolyte   74
10. Thread charts—BSW, BSF, UNC and UNF   88
11. Thread charts—metric   88
12. Thread charts—pipe thread (BSP)   89
13. Thread charts—British Association (BA)   89
14. Standard Wire Gauge sizes   97
15. Temper colours and temperatures   105
16. Selection of welding blowpipe nozzles   118
17. Blowpipe pressures for cutting   126
18. Typical current settings for electric welding electrodes   130
19. Basic settings for butt welds   134
20. Electric welding faults   139
21. Grades of abrasive sheet   144
22. Dimensions of pipe thread   158
23. Common sizes of copper water pipe   162
24. Common sizes of vee-belt   191
25. Wiring colours for a seven-pin plug   202
26. Metric conversion tables   217

Introduction

Farm Workshop is one of a set of four titles in the 'Farming Book Series'. The companion volumes are *Farm Machinery* by Brian Bell, and *Farm Crops* and *Farm Livestock* by Graham Boatfield. This book is designed to give the reader a sound, basic knowledge of workshop tools, equipment, processes and materials. There are sections dealing with welding, farm water supply and corrosion control. The final part of the book deals with both general and tractor repair work. There are suggested activities at the end of each chapter to encourage the reader to relate the text to his or her own experience at work.

Farm Workshop is suitable for the tractor driver who wishes to learn more about workshop techniques and for students taking courses leading to Phase I and II level examinations offered by City and Guilds and other regional examining bodies. The book will also be of value for private study by anyone interested in the establishment of a workshop, its equipment and the skills required to carry out routine maintenance and repairs. Tractor and machinery repair manuals, together with advanced specialist publications dealing with such topics as welding are recommended additional reading.

It is not always possible to give exact settings for a machine or a repair process in a book of this type. Average figures are given, purely as a guide, to illustrate typical settings and adjustments. Dimensions are given in metric units. Where alternative imperial figures are included, they may not be a direct conversion. In many instances, the conversion is an approximate equivalent.

A tidy workshop is a safer workshop.

Acknowledgements

My thanks are due to many people and companies for their help and advice in the preparation of this book. In particular, I thank Kevin O'Reilly for drawing many of the illustrations in the book and my colleague, Jeff Camplin, who read the manuscript during its early stages.

I also wish to thank the following companies. They have provided valuable technical information and allowed me to use a number of illustrations from their own publications.

Black & Decker Ltd, figs. 26, 28, 29, 63, 65.

B.O.C. Ltd, figs. 48–50, 52–6, 59–61.

David Brown Tractors Ltd, figs. 95–7.

Deltaflow Ltd, fig. 71.

J. H. Fenner Ltd, fig. 86.

Fordham Plastics Ltd, fig. 76 and the drawing on page 153.

Monoflow Lister Ltd.

James Neill Tools Ltd.

Ransomes, Sims & Jefferies Ltd, fig. 84.

Record Ridgway Ltd, figs. 17, 18, 31, 32, 64, 65.

Renold Ltd, figs. 87–91 and the drawing on page 182.

Martin J. Storey.

Wolf Electric Tools Ltd.

Yorkshire Imperial Fittings Ltd, figs. 67–70, 73.

Chapter 1

The Farm Workshop

EVERY FARM needs a workshop. The high cost of new machinery and ever-increasing repair bills are sufficient justification. The size and scope of that workshop will depend on three main factors: the size and type of farm, the interest and ability of the farm staff to carry out repair work and the distance from the farm to the local machinery dealer or repairer. It may be an existing building which has been converted or a new purpose-built one. Whatever the nature of the workshop it is essential that it has adequate equipment and that the users are trained in basic workshop skills. Local education authorities, the Agricultural Training Board and many tool and equipment suppliers offer suitable practical courses. Skills gained from such courses will prove invaluable because the range of work undertaken will include tractor and machinery maintenance, estate maintenance work and fabrication of new equipment. The mainly livestock farm can also reap benefit. Gates, crates and hoppers can be made or mended with a welding set; repairs and adaptations to water installations can be handled too.

There are, however, some jobs which must be left to the expert, particularly in the field of hydraulics and major tractor repairs. The purchase of expensive specialist tools, essential for such work, cannot be justified. All too often, the farm mechanic who takes on such specialised work has to bring in the dealer's mechanic to help out and the consequences of attempting such tasks with insufficient knowledge and equipment can be expensive.

Farm workshops vary from a small wooden hut with a basic set of tools to a large purpose-built structure with enough tackle to serve the large farm. To be effective, any workshop much meet certain requirements.

THE SITE AND BUILDING

Selecting the Site

The workshop should have a reasonably central site among the buildings, preferably close by the machinery storage shed and well away from livestock and straw barns. The workshop must have good access which allows for easy entry and exit of the largest farm machinery. A well-drained concrete area outside the building will provide parking and space for cleaning down machinery prior to overhaul. Fuel storage can conveniently be sited near the workshop. Adequate access must be provided for delivery tankers.

The Building

No two farm workshops will be the same. Nevertheless, there are basic points to be considered.

It should be constructed of *fire-resistant materials* such as brick or concrete blocks, or be a steel-framed building clad with corrugated metal or asbestos. Any framed building ought to be built with *solid walls* for the first metre or so from the ground. Asbestos, in particular, will not stand accidental battering from heavy metal components or runaway machines. The solid wall will also provide a surface for tool boards and anchorage for benches.

The doors should be high and wide enough to allow entry for large tractors and the combine harvester. Tractors and machines are getting bigger all the time, so allowance must be made for the future. A small door for personal entry should be provided so that the main doors do not have to be opened every time. Saving heat loss in this way is particularly important in the winter. Table 1 gives average dimensions of some of the more important farm machines and should be borne in mind when considering door size and floor area. Remember that even when they are open, the folding type of sliding door takes up quite a lot of the door opening width.

Buildings with *high roofs* should be avoided because they are difficult—and costly—to heat. Provided that the building is large enough for a combine harvester there is little benefit to be gained from

Table 1. Dimensions of some typical large farm machines

Type of machine		Length m	Width m	Height m
Tractors				
kW	hp			
45	60	3·7	1·8	2·7
67	90	4·4	2·2	2·8
90	120	5·1	2·5	3·0
187	250	6·4	3·5	3·6
Pick-up baler		5·0	2·75	1·5
Big round baler		4·3	2·4	2·7
Forage harvester		5·5	2·5	3·5
Combine harvester:				
2·6 m cut		7·6	3·0	3·4
3·66 m cut		8·1	3·9	3·5
4·88 m cut		8·75	5·2*	3·75

* Note—the overall width is reduced to 4·25 metres with the table removed.

excessive height. Heating costs can be further saved by making within the main workshop, a smaller enclosed area whose roof—constructed to carry a load—will serve as a storage loft. This small workshop will provide a comfortable work area with benches, welding equipment and fixed power tools. Provided that the door is large enough, assemblies removed from machines during overhaul can be brought in here for repair.

The workshop should have a *level concrete floor*. A very smooth surface should be avoided because patches of oil or grease on such surfaces will turn the floor into a skating rink. Wooden duck boards placed on the floor in front of benches, pedestal drills, grinders and other fixed equipment will help to insulate the mechanic's feet during long periods of bench work. A good safety measure is to anchor the duck boards to the floor. The size of the floor area will be ruled by the building selected for conversion or by finance available for a new building.

When planning a workshop remember to allow plenty of space to get round the machine which has been brought in for repair. For this reason, benches and fixed equipment are best concentrated in one area of the workshop. A steel rack along one wall will provide storage for lengths of steel, water pipe and timber.

All workshops need a *welding bay* whose wall surfaces should have a dark, non-reflective finish. It should be equipped with a steel welding bench and a storage cabinet for welding rods; provision should be made for fume extraction. Screens, portable for preference, should be used to protect others from the flash of the arc welder because anyone looking at the glare is likely to suffer from 'arc eye'—a very painful experience. Anyone wearing contact lenses must avoid looking at the direct glare of an arc welder.

Heat, Light and Power

Adequate heat is essential, much of the overhaul work being done during slack periods in the winter. Portable gas, oil or electric heaters can be directed at the mechanic who is working on machines in the main area of the workshop. A more permanent installation—gas or electric heater fixed in a safe position or a slow-combustion stove—should be provided near the benches and fixed workshop equipment. Some form of insulation should be considered, and here again, a small enclosed workshop within the main building with loft storage above will be easier and cheaper to heat, and the loft floor will provide a degree of insulation.

Ventilation should be provided in the form of windows which can be opened in warm weather. The fumes from engine exhausts are poisonous and provision must be made for their extraction. Whereas open windows will be sufficient for a small, single-cylinder engine, if larger engines are to be run for test purposes it is a good idea to fix up an exhaust pipe extension which passes through a wall of the workshop. A flexible pipe can be placed over the vehicle exhaust before the engine is started so that the fumes will be piped outside where they can cause no harm.

Good *lighting* is very important. Large windows, especially in the bench area, are necessary to provide plenty of natural light. This should be supplemented by electric lighting to give a good level of illumination throughout the workshop. As a general guide, ten square metres of floor area require about 600 watts of filament bulbs or 130 watts if fluorescent tubes are used. Additional strip lights should be installed over workbenches and fixed equipment. The walls and ceiling will reflect both natural and artificial light if they are painted white or at least a light colour.

Inspection lamps, fitted with well-insulated cable, complete the lighting requirements in the workshop. They are generally 240 volt lamps and are quite safe to use provided that they are kept in good condition, are properly earthed and never used without the bulb guard in place. It is best to clip an inspection lamp in position with the handle grip; hanging the lamp on a hook through the bulb guard can be dangerous. Low-voltage inspection lamps are safer still. They require a separate low-voltage circuit, powered by a transformer connected to the mains. A floodlight outside the workshop will be useful during the winter months.

Nearly all power tools are electric. Sometimes, compressed air or an engine-driven line shaft with belt pulleys are used to provide the power. Plenty of well-spaced fused *socket outlets* should be installed, reducing the need for long extension leads trailing across the workshop floor. Extension cables are easily damaged and must not be used in this condition. Farms with three-phase supply will gain advantage in the workshop but this form of electric power is not essential except for the very large pedestal drills, heavy-duty grinders and high-capacity welding sets. The mechanic who needs a high-output electric welder can always use a generator-powered machine where mains supply is unsuitable.

STORES

Storage of tools, materials and spare parts deserves some attention. There is little worse than a workshop bench so cluttered with tools, metal off-cuts and miscellaneous bits and pieces that there is no space to do any work.

Use wall space above the benches for tool boards. Putting only one tool on each peg makes checking for missing items a simple matter. To help keep the tools in the proper place a shadow board with silhouettes of the tools can be made. An alternative is a portable tool trolley which can be moved around the workshop. The toolbox will also be used for tool storage but it should not be the home for files, measuring and marking tools or items which have infrequent use. Good tools are expensive—it will cost several hundred pounds to provide hand and power tools for even a moderately equipped workshop. Careful storage will help to ensure that your tools last for many years.

Materials and miscellaneous spares are best stored in racks or bins. A steel rack can be built on one of the workshop walls. Make sure that it is made in a way which allows easy storage and removal of steel—the merchant will supply metal in lengths of seven metres upwards and quite a lot of space is needed to handle it. Wooden or metal bins will provide storage for spare parts, stocks of which should be kept to the minimum. Every farm workshop has a pile of obsolete spares and experience will show which items are worth keeping in stock. Among the essential stores are nuts, bolts, washers and split pins, most of which can be purchased in boxed assortments. The box can be refilled from time to time with further supplies packed in individual sizes. Screw-top jars or tins, with the lids fixed to the underside of a shelf, make excellent storage for small items such as keys, circlips and grease nipples.

Parts removed from tractors and machinery during overhaul should also be stored with care. Plastic stacking boxes or home-made trays are ideal and will save time and temper because, with luck, all the parts will come to hand when they are required.

Fuel and Lubricants

The fuel store can conveniently be situated near the workshop. Petrol must not be stored in bulk unless it is in an underground tank and the installation meets statutory requirements. Petrol stored in a can for

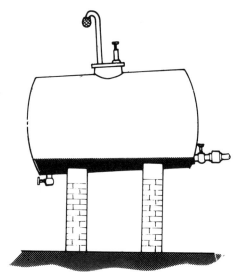

Fig. 1. A typical diesel fuel storage system

a lawn mower or other small engine must be kept in a place where there is no fire risk. Two-stroke mixture for chain saws will also be needed. Make sure that cans for both of these fuels are clearly marked.

Diesel fuel may be stored above or below ground. An electric pump will be needed for underground storage but gravity filling is normal from tanks above ground level.

Diesel engines need clean fuel for long, trouble-free service. The storage system must be good enough to ensure the fuel remains in the same clean condition as it leaves the delivery tanker.

The tank should be high enough to allow gravity filling. It should be sited to allow easy access for the delivery tanker, tractors and self-propelled farm machinery.

The base of the tank should slope away from the draw-off point. A sludge cock at the lower end of the tank is used to drain off water (caused by condensation inside the tank) and sludge before a new delivery of fuel arrives. The storage tank must not be galvanised because diesel fuel attacks the zinc coating.

An airtight cover should be fitted on the filler opening. A ventilation pipe in the top of the tank will allow air to enter when fuel is drawn off, restrict the entry of dirt and keep rainwater out. A dipstick or sight tube is needed to check the fuel level.

When a new delivery of fuel is expected, all tractor tanks should be filled. Open the sludge cock and allow all the sediment to drain off. After delivery, leave the fuel to settle for twenty-four hours before use.

To reduce formation of water through condensation in tractor fuel tanks it is a good idea to fill the tank at the end of the day's work, especially if the tractor is stored outside or in an open-fronted building.

Lubricants should be stored in a way which keeps them clean. Some oil companies supply oil storage cabinets, complete with hand pumps. Drum storage will be adequate for most farms.

It is cheaper to buy oil in bulk drums, rather than in the smaller 25 litre (5 gallon) containers. The larger drums can be stored on their sides, on purpose-made stands. A tap fitted to the drum can be used to draw off the oil into jugs. It is important to keep all containers used for oil in a clean condition, a small cupboard being suitable for the purpose.

Set aside an area for lubricants, preferably in the stores, and in any case, well away from welding and other activities where there is a fire risk. Keep the tops of oil containers clean and replace caps on the drums after use. These precautions are important because dust and grit must not be allowed to contaminate the oil.

SAFETY IN THE WORKSHOP

Poor working conditions, unsafe tools, faulty electrical equipment and untidy benches all contribute to accidents. A few precautions, together with a clean and tidy work area, will go a long way towards reducing the risk of an injury in your workshop.

It is a good idea to consult the local Farm Safety Officer at the planning stage of a new workshop. His advice should also be sought if there is any doubt about the regulations applying to an existing workshop.

Good lighting is very important. The work benches should be clean and uncluttered. The building must be warm enough to allow work to proceed in reasonable comfort: cold hands graze or bruise very easily when a spanner slips or the hammer is slightly off target.

Tools

The condition of your tools, especially chisels, screwdrivers, hammers and files, should be checked at regular intervals. Mushroom-headed chisels and punches should be restored to the correct shape. Tighten loose hammer heads with an extra wedge. Throw away any spanners with stretched or cracked jaws and scrap any adjustable spanners which are worn.

Don't wrap your fingers tightly round a spanner, especially when attempting to slacken off a tight nut or bolt. Apply the pressure with the palm of the hand, then if the spanner slips there is much less risk of losing the skin from your knuckles. A spanner, or any other tool, will slip if it is in contact with a rusty, greasy or dirty surface. Be safe, clean off the dirt first. Tools with insulated handles for electrical work must be stored carefully and checked for condition. A shock from a vehicle electrical system may be unpleasant but a shock from the mains can be fatal. Always disconnect the supply before working with any type of electrical equipment.

Power tools must be well maintained to keep them safe. Never use an electric tool unless it is earthed correctly or double insulated. This is most important when using power tools outside where cables trail across damp ground. Check all cables, plugs and sockets frequently and replace any damaged items immediately. Shatterproof, rubberised plugs should be used for power tools. Some socket outlets may have to withstand damp conditions. For these applications, use a socket outlet designed for the purpose which is insulated, splashproof and has a protective flap to keep moisture out when the socket is not in use.

Extension cables should be as short as possible and if the cable is coiled on a drum, it should be completely unreeled to stop the wire overheating. It is better to install some extra sockets rather than have extension leads trailing across benches and floors.

Fuses will blow from time to time. They must only be replaced by another of the same amp rating.

Goggles must be worn for eye protection when grinding or chipping at metal and other materials. There are important safety regulations which apply to fitting abrasive wheels on grinders and these must be observed. The regulations include instructions about the material used for grinding wheels related to machine speed and the procedure for fitting the wheels to the spindles (see page 66). The work rest must be close to the grinder wheel. Some grinders have a spark guard made of transparent material; even so, it is still a sensible precaution to wear goggles, especially if there are likely to be a lot of sparks. Keep the goggles on a peg near the grinder when they are not in use.

When drilling a hole with an electric drill, make sure the work is held in a vice or clamped to a bench if there is any risk of the metal moving while drilling is in progress. Without this precaution the metal might pick up on the drill bit and turn with it. This is dangerous, the drill bit is likely to snap off and there is a real risk of personal injury.

Electric Shock

The surest way to avoid electric shock is never to work with live electrical equipment. No matter how many precautions are taken, there will still be people who suffer a shock. If this happens to someone else while you are near some rapid action is needed. The current should be switched off immediately if this is possible. Never attempt to move a person who is in contact with a high-voltage electric current, above 650 volts. When attempting to release someone still in contact with lower voltages, e.g. 240 or 415, do not touch the person directly on the skin because you may also receive a shock. Pull the person free with something dry and non-conducting such as rubber gloves, dry wood or clothing. Once the victim is free, apply artificial respiration if necessary and send for help. Artificial respiration is a skill best learned from a qualified first-aid instructor. Posters about dealing with electric shock are available and one ought to be on prominent display in every farm workshop.

Compressed Air

Never direct compressed air at the body—it can cause serious injury. When compressed air is used to dry off parts which have been washed or to remove deposits of dry dirt, always direct the air away from yourself. It is also a sensible precaution to wear goggles. Spray painting with compressed air is another hazard. Always wear a good-quality mask.

Welding

Never look directly at the glare of an electric welder. The brilliance of the arc will cause a painful eye condition known as 'arc-eye'. Don't wear contact lenses in an electric welding shop either.

Use a purpose-made mask when doing electric welding and never chip at welding slag without using a clear glass face mask or goggles. Oxy-acetylene welding goggles are not suitable for electric welding and must not be worn for that purpose.

Take precautions when welding to avoid setting fire to anything and only handle freshly welded parts with a pair of suitable tongs. Protective clothing for welding should include a welding mask, welding apron, safety footwear and some welding gloves.

Jacks

Always apply the hand brake and chock the wheels of a tractor or other vehicle before it is jacked up. When removing a wheel, remember to slacken the wheel nuts before the wheel is lifted clear of the ground. Axle stands or sound wooden blocks should be used to support the machine before anyone goes underneath to carry out an inspection or repair. Never use bricks or concrete blocks—they may crumble or slip. Don't leave a machine jacked up for long periods without any other means of support because the jack might slip or someone might let it down accidentally. Always keep jacks well maintained and in good condition.

Working with Engines

Exhaust fumes contain carbon monoxide—a poisonous gas. Always open the workshop doors when an engine is running except when the building has a purpose-made extraction system which pipes the fumes away.

Never wrap your thumb around the starting handle of an engine; keep it close by the fingers. Should the engine kick back while being started, an incorrect hold could result in a broken wrist or thumb, or both.

Take great care when removing radiator caps from hot engines. Turn the cap slowly and, to be really safe from scalding, place a piece of sacking or thick cloth over the cap before it is undone.

Personal Protection

The best clothing for workshop use is a boiler suit. Long, flowing clothes can involve the wearer in serious accidents, especially when working with power tools and moving machinery.

Wear substantial footwear. Ordinary boots or shoes offer little protection against falling objects. Safety boots, or shoes, with steel toecaps are ideal for the workshop. Heavily studded boots can be dangerous on oily floors or when climbing over the slippery metal surfaces of large machines.

Dermatitis is a very unpleasant skin infection, often caused by petrol, diesel fuel, lubricants and similar materials. To reduce the risk of infection it is a wise precaution to apply barrier cream to the hands before starting work. Use a good-quality hand cleanser to remove all traces of oil and grease after work is completed. On the other hand it is not a good idea to wash hands in petrol which removes the natural oils from the skin and increases the risk of dermatitis.

Take special care when working on equipment such as sprayers which may be contaminated with chemicals. They should be cleaned thoroughly prior to overhaul and the mechanic should wear suitable protective clothing, including rubber gloves, for the cleaning operation.

Fire

Fire extinguishers must be easily accessible. It is important to understand which type of extinguisher should be used for which sort of fire because it can be fatal to use a water-based extinguisher on a fire caused by an electrical fault. Switch off the mains supply to the building before tackling any fire and call the fire brigade. The main isolator switch for the building should be clearly marked and easy to reach.

There are several different types of fire extinguisher. Make sure you can identify the different types and that you know how to use them.

- *Dry powder and carbon dioxide extinguishers* can be used to tackle live electrical fires and burning liquids. They are also suitable for small fires involving wood, paper and similar materials.
- *Foam extinguishers* must not be used on live electrical fires because the foam is a conductor of electricity and the user could be electrocuted. Foam extinguishers can be used to tackle burning liquids and fires involving small quantities of wood, paper and similar materials.
- *Soda acid extinguishers* are water based and must not be used for live electrical fires or burning liquids such as oil, grease and paint. This type of extinguisher is best suited to tackle burning timber, paper and other materials.
- *Gas pressure extinguishers* are water based. When gas is released inside the extinguisher, it forces a jet of water from the appliance. It, too, is not suitable for burning liquids and live electrical fires.

There are two other fire fighting aids which should be in the farm workshop. Fire buckets, containing sand, can be used to smother small outbreaks. Buckets of water can be kept in the workshop too, but remember the limitations concerning the use of water to fight fires. An asbestos smothering blanket, stored in a special container fixed to a wall, is another useful fire fighting aid.

It is better to prevent fires. A few simple precautions will pay dividends. These include:

- Store fuel and lubricants well away from welding equipment and any other possible source of fire.
- Never oil the threads of oxy-acetylene welding gauges and hoses. This action can cause an explosion.
- Keep all electrical equipment in good condition. Don't overload wiring circuits. Electrical faults are one of the main causes of fire.
- There are many flammable liquids in the workshop. Don't smoke where there is petrol, paint thinners, propane, butane etc. Any spillages should be cleared up quickly.

- Don't inspect a battery on charge with a naked flame. Batteries give off hydrogen and oxygen during the charging process. These gases are flammable.
- Disconnect battery terminals on vehicles before carrying out repairs.

First Aid

In order to comply with the Farm Safety Regulations there must be a first-aid box on the farm. Its contents will vary with the number of employees. A leaflet is available from the Farm Safety Officer which lists the bandages and ointments which should be included, and the box must also contain a copy of the official farm safety leaflet about first aid. At least one member of the farm staff should have some basic first-aid training.

THINGS TO DO

1. Check through your toolkit at regular intervals. Make sure that all your tools are in good condition. Scrap any which are worn or dangerous.
2. Learn how to stop and start the power tools in a workshop you are familiar with.
3. Always wear goggles when using a grinder.
4. Always place an axle stand or wooden blocks under a jacked-up machine before going underneath to carry out repairs.
5. Make sure you know the location of all the fire extinguishers on your farm.

QUESTIONS

1. What important factors should be considered when designing a new farm workshop?
2. Why is it dangerous to run an engine in a closed workshop?
3. Describe a suitable storage installation for tractor diesel fuel.
4. What is dermatitis?
5. Which types of fire extinguisher are suitable for use against a fire involving a live electrical appliance?

Chapter 2

Workshop Tools

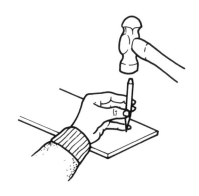

THIS CHAPTER surveys the range of hand and power tools, together with the fixed equipment available for the farm workshop. Many of the tools are essential equipment for all but the most basic workshops. Selection, care and use of these tools are considered.

HAND TOOLS: SPANNERS

Open-ended spanners can be purchased singly or in sets. Sets of BSW, A/F and Metric spanners are required, as all of these bolt types will be found on farms for a while yet. An open-ended spanner is not very convenient for working in confined spaces. It must be moved for at least one-sixth of a turn before the spanner can be repositioned on a nut, this is not always possible. Use the correct size of spanner. Careless use or ill-fitting spanners may cause sore knuckles. Do not wrap the hand around an open-ended spanner when undoing a nut; apply firm pressure with the palm of the hand. In this way there is less risk of injury should the spanner slip off a nut.

Ring spanners are safer to use because the spanner fits right around the nut. They are more suitable for working in confined spaces, only

one-twelfth of a turn being needed before the spanner may be re
positioned on the nut. Some ring spanners are flat but most have double
offset ends at 30° or 45°. A 30° offset is less likely to slip. Two examples
of special types of ring spanners are short-handled ones for work in very
tight spaces and those with a slot cut through the ring for working on
pipe unions. The slit spanner can be slipped over the pipe and placed on
the union nut.

Combination spanners offer both the above types on the one tool
which has an open jaw at one end and a ring at the other. Both ends of
the spanner are for the same size of nut.

Box spanners, more commonly known as *plug spanners*, are a cheap,
but quite effective, form of socket spanner. Designed for hexagonal
nuts, they have only six faces, and are turned with a steel rod called a
tommy bar. By comparison, a ring spanner has twelve faces—it is
classed as a bi-hexagon spanner. A box spanner to fit sparking plugs and
a few large-size box spanners for tackling such items as tractor wheel
nuts will be valuable items for the toolkit.

Allen keys are hexagonal in section and 'L' shaped. They are used
with Allen screws which have a recessed hexagonal socket head. There
are sizes to fit both British and Metric bolts.

Adjustable spanners. Every toolbox has one or more of these all-
purpose spanners. However, a worn adjustable spanner with stretched
jaws is a dangerous tool. It will slip off tight nuts, taking off the corners
and sometimes the skin off the user's fingers. It is best to use an
adjustable only as a last resort. When the spanner is worn, throw it
away. Its useful life can be extended by proper use: fit the spanner on the
nut so that the solid jaw takes the strain; excess pressure on the moving
jaw will soon stretch the adjusting thread.

Sockets may be rather more expensive than ring and open-end
spanners but they are excellent for high-speed work. Sockets can be
used to get at nuts in recessed holes and similar awkward places. Most
sockets are bi-hexagon with twelve faces. The common size of socket
has a $\frac{1}{2}$ in square drive. A $\frac{1}{2}$ in square hole in the socket is used to connect
it to various extension bars, a tee-handle, speed brace, ratchet and even
a torque wrench. A small universal coupling fixed in the socket drive
makes it possible to turn a nut with the handle at an angle to the socket.

Although sockets with $\frac{1}{2}$ in square drive are by far the most popular
size, other sizes of square drive are also made. Miniature $\frac{1}{4}$ in drive
socket sets are handy for vehicle and similar work. The sockets are made
for BA sizes and up to about $\frac{1}{4}$ in BSW, $\frac{1}{2}$ in A/F and 15 mm Metric.
Screwdriver type handles, with or without a built-in rachet mechanism,
as well as tee-bars, extension bars and ratchet handles are made for use
with these small sockets. Sockets with a $\frac{3}{8}$ in square drive are made too.

Heavy-duty socket sets with $\frac{3}{4}$ in or 1 in square drive meet the needs of

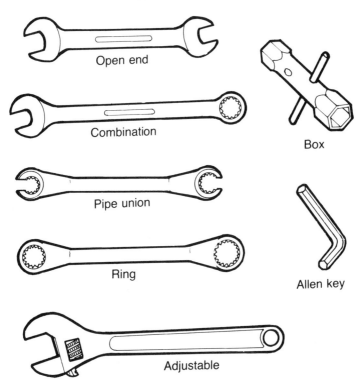

Open end

Combination

Box

Pipe union

Ring

Allen key

Adjustable

Fig. 2. Spanners

heavy engineering. A typical 1 in drive metric set has ten sockets ranging in size from 36 mm to 80 mm. A set like this is very expensive and has few applications on the farm.

Power-drive sockets are specially designed for use with impact tools and other power-driven equipment. A farm workshop equipped with a suitable air compressor can take advantage of the rapid operation of impact tools. The drive unit looks rather like a small electric hand drill. It can be used with sockets to tighten nuts and bolts to a preset torque. Power-drive sockets usually have a single hexagon recess and are much tougher than hand-drive sockets. Ordinary sockets should not be used with power tools.

Torque wrenches are used to tighten nuts and bolts to a required torque (tightness) and most torque wrenches are adjustable over a range of settings. Torque is the turning force applied, in this case, to a nut or stud. Certain components, such as engine cylinder heads and

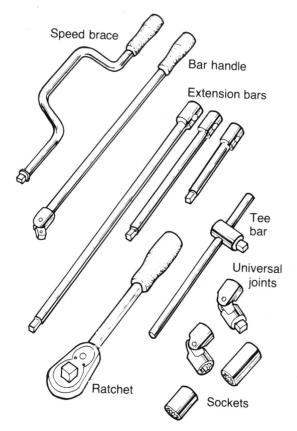

Fig. 3. Socket spanners

bearing caps, must have their retaining bolts tightened accurately to the correct setting. So although this is a tool which will have little use in a general workshop it is essential if more advanced work, including engine overhauls, is carried out.

The cheapest form of torque wrench has a pointer attached to its toughened, flexible steel handle. When a nut is tightened, the handle will bend gradually and the pointer indicates on a scale how much torque has been applied. More expensive wrenches have an adjustable locking mechanism built into the handle. When the torque applied to the bolt reaches the preset level, the mechanism is released and a clicking noise is heard. The wrench reloads itself automatically when pressure on the handle is released.

Spanner Sizes

Spanners for BSW and BSF nuts and bolts are marked with a size which relates to the diameter of the bolt. A spanner which fits a $\frac{1}{2}$ in Whitworth bolt will have jaws much wider than half an inch.

ANC and ANF threads, used on machinery of American origin, require A/F spanners (A/F means across flats; a $\frac{1}{2}$ in A/F spanner measures half an inch across the jaws). The same A/F spanners will also fit UNC and UNF bolts.

Metric nuts require different spanners. These have markings which give the measurement between the jaws in millimetres.

BA spanners are marked with the size of the bolt, for example 6 BA.

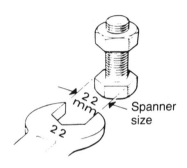

Fig. 4. Spanner size

Safe Use of Spanners

- To make identification easy keep Whitworth, A/F and Metric spanners separate from each other. Mark each type with a different colour paint for instant recognition. Hang your spanners on a toolboard—this makes it simple to check on losses.
- Don't use packing to make the spanner fit—find the correct spanner.
- Don't hit spanners with a hammer or extend them with a piece of pipe. You may strip the thread or break the bolt, and the spanner will be damaged as well. Use ring spanners or sockets on stubborn nuts and bolts. Penetrating oil will help when dealing with rusty or seized nuts.
- Keep sparking plug sockets square on the plug as sideways pressure may crack the porcelain insulation.
- Do not use a spanner with bent, twisted or stretched jaws.
- Keep your spanners clean. Dirty or greasy spanners cause accidents.

SCREWDRIVERS

There are several different types and size of screwdriver. They are intended for turning screws or bolts with slotted heads and should not be used for work which will damage the point or bend the blade.

The *Cabinetmaker's* screwdriver is a carpenter's tool. It has a wooden handle, usually beech or ash, which must not be hit with a hammer. It is not suitable for mains electrical work.

An *Engineer's* screwdriver may have a round or a square blade fitted in a tough plastic handle. It is sometimes desirable to give the handle of a screwdriver a sharp tap with a hammer when trying to loosen a badly rusted screw, in which case an engineer's screwdriver can be used. When dealing with a very tight screw, a small spanner can be put on the square part of the blade; the screwdriver is pushed firmly into the slot and the spanner is used to turn the blade.

Electrician's screwdrivers have insulated handles, made of Bakelite or toughened plastic. They are intended for work with mains installations as well as vehicle electrics. However, always turn off the supply before starting work. An electrician's screwdriver is similar to an engineer's screwdriver but smaller in size. Many engineer's screwdrivers are also suitable for electrical work.

Crosspoint screwdrivers are made for use with either Phillips or Posidrive screw heads. The handles are usually tough plastic but some

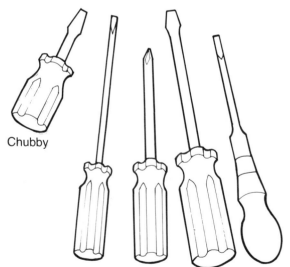

Chubby

Electrician's Crosspoint Engineer's Cabinetmaker's

Fig. 5. Screwdrivers

re wood. The advantage of this type of screwdriver is that the screw retains the recess shape well and considerable force can be applied to a tight screw.

London screwdrivers have long, wide blades. They are ideal for loosening large or very tight screws.

A double-ended *Right-Angle* screwdriver, with both straight and crosspoint blades, will on some occasions be very useful for getting at screws in awkward places.

Ratchet screwdrivers are used in high-speed work. There are two types; one has a two-way ratchet built into the handle so that a simple adjustment allows for screws to be loosened or tightened when the handle is turned. The other has a spiral ratchet mechanism, also with a selector for slackening or tightening screws. When the screwdriver handle is pushed downwards, the blade is turned by the spiral mechanism. These screwdrivers are not suitable for very tight screws.

Screwdriver Sizes

The length of the metal blade determines screwdriver size. Blade width varies too. A typical range of engineer's screwdrivers will have sizes from 102 mm long × 8 mm width up to 305 mm × 9·5 mm (4 in × ½ in to 12 in × ⅜ in). Electrician's screwdrivers are made in somewhat smaller sizes. A short, stubby screwdriver with a blade length of about 38 mm (1½ in) is a useful addition to any toolkit.

Crosspoint screwdrivers are made in four sizes, No. 1 being the smallest and No. 4 the largest.

Using Screwdrivers

- Sharpening is best done with a file. When a grindstone is used great care must be taken to ensure the end of the blade does not overheat, making it brittle. The tip of the blade should be flat and square as shown in the diagram. Never sharpen a screwdriver to a knife edge.

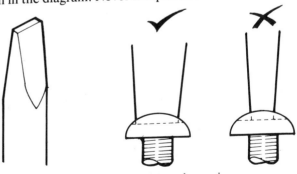

Fig. 6. Screwdriver sharpening

- Avoid the use of a worn screwdriver, the rounded corners soon ru̶
  screw slots.
- Always use the correct size of screwdriver for the job in hand. Yo̶
  will damage the screw slot if the blade is too small.
- The quickest way to ruin a screwdriver is to use it as a chisel, lever c̶
  scraper. It is not intended for stirring paint either! With correc̶
  sharpening and careful use, a screwdriver will last for a long time.

HAMMERS

A good hammer will be made of high-quality carbon steel. It will have a̶
hard, polished striking face and the head will be fitted on a hickor̶
handle. A less expensive timber used for hammer handles, or shafts, i̶
ash. The hammer head is held tightly on the shaft with wedges made o̶
hardwood or steel.

Ball pein or *engineer's hammers* are basic workshop tools. A ball pei̶
hammer has a flat striking face at one end of the head and a ball at the̶
other, the ball being used for riveting. Hammer size is measured by the̶
weight of the head, ball pein hammers commonly ranging from 230 gm̶
to 1·4 kg (½ lb to 3 lb) although sometimes it is possible to find heavier
examples. A set of different weight ball pein hammers is needed to deal
with farm repairs.

The *cross pein* or *Warrington pattern hammer* has a head with a blunt
chisel-shaped end opposite to the flat face and is really a carpenter's
tool. The cross pein end is useful for starting tacks and small nails in
timber while they are held between the finger and thumb.

The *claw hammer*, also a carpenter's tool, can be purchased with a
wooden or steel handle. The claw end is ideal for removing nails from
timber.

The *pin hammer* is a very small ball pein or cross pein hammer with a
head weight of approximately 110 gm (¼ lb). Mainly used for driving in
tacks and panel pins, it is also handy for cutting out small paper gaskets,
especially the holes in the gaskets.

Club hammers or *lump hammers*, part of a bricklayer's toolkit, are
handy in the farm workshop for some of the heavy work. Useful sizes
are 1·1 kg and 1·8 kg (2½ lb and 4 lb).

A *sledge hammer* is essential farm workshop equipment. A few
well-placed blows with a sledge hammer will soon straighten a bent
component, especially if it is held on an anvil. Most sledge hammers are
double-faced and should, for preference, have a hickory handle.
Typical sizes are 3·15, 4·5 and 6·3 kg (7, 10 and 14 lb).

Soft-faced hammers should be used when working with parts which
might be damaged by an engineer's hammer, especially castings, brass.

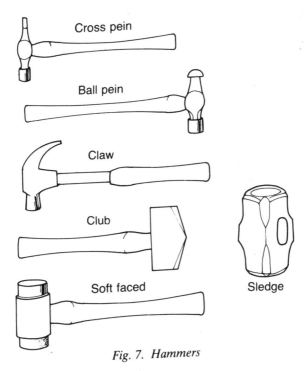

Fig. 7. Hammers

copper and similar soft materials. The striking faces are made of copper, hide, tough plastic or rubber and can be renewed when damaged or worn. The size of a soft-faced hammer is described by the head diameter; 38 mm and 50 mm (1½ in and 2 in) are typical.

Selecting Hammers

A basic set of hammers for the farm workshop should include 450 gm and 1.1 kg ball pein hammers, a 450 gm steel-handled claw hammer and a 3·15 kg or 4·5 kg sledge hammer. Useful additions to the list are a 50 mm diameter soft-faced hammer with copper and hide faces, a 230 gm ball pein or a pin hammer for gasket making and a 1·8 kg club hammer. Keep them all on a tool board so that you can find them when they are wanted.

Using Hammers

● Always hold a hammer near the end of its handle and let your wrist form a pivot point. The hammer face should be parallel with the object being struck when it makes contact. For several reasons holding the hammer shaft near the head should be avoided: the hammer face will not strike the work squarely, less force will be applied and you may bruise or dent the surface of the work piece. Strangling a hammer—holding it by the neck—is both inefficient and unsafe.

- Never use a hammer with a loose head or damaged handle. Always keep the hammer shaft clean and dry. A loose head can be tightened with an extra wedge in the handle or by soaking the head and handle in water. It is important that the head is fitted so that it is not twisted in relation to the handle. You will need to reduce it slightly in size by carefully removing an equal thickness of wood all the way round the handle to ensure that the head fits straight and square. A hammer with a badly fitted head is difficult to use with any degree of accuracy. Once a good fit is attained, secure the head firmly in position with wedges. Finally smooth off the end of the shaft so that it is a flush fit with the head.

- Hammer faces are very hard. Avoid banging two hammer faces together because this can crack or damage them. There is also the risk of a flying chip of metal causing an eye injury.

- Use the correct size of hammer for the job in hand. It is always better to use a fairly heavy hammer when straightening a component or removing a part. For example, a light hammer may only burr over the end of a shaft which must be removed while a heavier one will achieve the objective with a few sharp blows. For work with castings, use a soft-faced hammer or an engineer's hammer and a suitable punch made of copper or some other soft material.

- When using a hammer, keep your eye on the work, not on the hammer head. Practise using a hammer by driving some nails into a hard piece of timber. With the proper hold, the correct action and by keeping your eye on the nail, you will be able to drive it home without bending it.

- Claw hammers are useful for removing nails, steel-handled hammers being better for large nails which may loosen, or even break, a wooden shaft. A small block of wood under the hammer head will make nail removal easier and will prevent damage to the surface of the wood. For really big nails, it is best to use a wrecking bar. This has a chisel-shaped prybar at one end and a nail-drawing claw at the other. They are made in various lengths.

PLIERS AND GRIPS

Combination or *engineer's pliers* will be found in every toolkit. The jaws have a flat face for holding flat material and a rounded section for gripping bolts and other round-section material. The inner part of the jaws have a pair of knife edges for wire cutting. Most combination pliers have slots on the outside of the jaws, near the hinge. They have a shearing action when the handles are closed and are used for cutting soft wire. Combination pliers are suitable for straightening, bending, gripping, twisting, cutting and turning small components and wire. They are not meant for tightening small bolts and screws.

Electrician's pliers are similar to engineer's combination pliers but have heavily insulated handles.

Side-cutting pliers or *diagonal-cutting pliers* are used for cutting wire, split pins and small nails. Other suitable work includes removing old split pins when dismantling farm equipment and stripping the insulation off electric cable. Always use the strongest part of the cutting edge which is near the rivet. This also gives maximum leverage on the

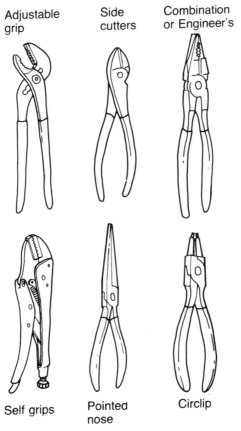

Fig. 8. *Pliers and grips*

handles. *End-cutting pliers* are another type of wire cutter. For best results and maximum life, always cut with the central part of the jaws.

Long-nose pliers have rather limited use. They are handy for getting at small parts in confined spaces and for removing some types of circlip. The tips of long-nose pliers are not strong enough for heavy work. If severely overloaded, they will break off.

Circlip pliers, used for fitting or removing circlips to shafts and housings, are made in two patterns, one for internal circlips and the other for the external type. Some circlip pliers are adjustable, others are supplied with a set of different size points. These pliers may have infrequent use but they can save time and temper.

Adjustable grips are useful for holding parts which are too big for combination pliers. The cheapest type is similar to combination pliers but the hinge has a slip joint, giving the choice of two jaw opening widths. Other slip-joint pliers with up to six jaw settings are handy for gripping quite large material including pipework. *Self-grip wrenches* can be used to lock two parts together or to grip on to almost any section of metal. A screw adjustment provides a range of jaw settings. Once the jaw width is set the grips are locked in position with a lever. A release lever is used to remove the grips when the work is complete. In an emergency, self-grips will serve as an adjustable spanner.

Most workshops will have a pair of *Stillsons*; these are adjustable grips for use with round bar and pipe. Stillson wrenches with a jaw capacity of up to 125 mm (5 in) are readily available from toolshops but do not use them as spanners as they will soon turn any hexagon-headed bolt into scrap metal!

Chain and *strap wrenches*, suitable for gripping large-diameter pipe-work and many other items, are available in several sizes. A chain wrench consists of a steel handle with a piece of roller chain attached near the end. The chain is wrapped around the work and then threaded through a slot at the end of the tool; when the handle is turned, the chain grips the workpiece to tighten or loosen it as required. Generally smaller and with a piece of strap instead of chain, the strap wrench is used for removing or fitting oil filter elements of the screw-in type. Both chain and strap wrenches could be made in the farm workshop.

Selecting Pliers

Pliers are classified by length. A typical range of combination pliers has sizes from 125 mm to 250 mm (5 to 10 in) and a pair 175 mm (7 in) long will normally be suitable. Most other types of plier are available in sizes up to 175 mm. Adjustable grips vary in size according to pattern and purpose. Self-grip wrenches are made in two or three sizes; a pair 250 mm long with a jaw capacity of 28 mm will serve most purposes.

Using Pliers

- Always use pliers with insulated handles when working with electrical equipment and don't forget to turn off the mains supply first.
- Select the correct size and type for the job and don't use pliers as a substitute for a hammer or a lever. The jaws and cutting edges are very hard and such misuse may damage them.
- Pliers are often used to hold small parts while they are welded. Keep an old pair for this work as excessive overheating will spoil a good pair.
- Extra care is needed with long-nose pliers because the points will snap off if subjected to too much leverage.
- Keep all pliers clean and rust free, especially at the hinge. Protect the handles of insulated pliers; don't store them loose in a toolbox with sharp-edged tools.

PUNCHES

Although a selection of punches can be purchased from tool shops, many mechanics prefer to make their own from worn shafts and old valve stems. Pieces of brass rod will make soft punches for working with castings and parts made of soft metal.

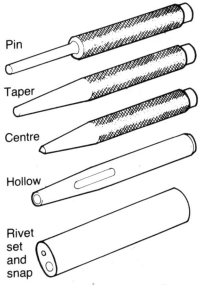

Pin

Taper

Centre

Hollow

Rivet set and snap

Fig. 9. Types of punch

Taper punches are handy for lining up holes when joining two or more parts with bolts or rivets. They can be used for driving bolts, rivets and pins out of holes. Their shape makes taper punches unsuitable for dealing with long bolts and pins.

Pin punches or *parallel punches* are better for removing bolts and pins. They are made of hard steel and, the smaller sizes in particular, will snap off if used as a lever.

A *Centre punch* is used to mark the centre spot when drilling a hole in metal, the impression made by the punch helping to start the drill bit. Centre punches should be sharpened with a grindstone so that the angle of the point is about 50°. Marking parts during overhaul to ensure correct reassembly is another use for a centre punch.

Marking punches are a luxury item. Sets of both number and letter punches are made with different size characters.

Rivet snaps are a special type of punch. The end face has a hole shaped like the head of a round-head rivet. Some rivet snaps also have a 'set' which is a parallel hole which fits over the shank of the rivet. Snaps and sets are made for common sizes of rivet. Some mechanics use a small riveting anvil, held in a vice; it has a hollow in its surface which fits a rivet head.

After the rivet is in position, the set is used to drive close together the parts which are to be joined. Next, the rivet is swelled in the holes with a hammer. The snap is used to do the final tightening and provide a neat finish.

Selecting and Using Punches

Punches are made in various lengths and diameters. A useful set of taper punches would contain sizes from 3 mm to 12 mm in diameter. Pin punches from 1·5 mm to 9·5 mm ($\frac{1}{16}$–$\frac{3}{8}$ in) will meet most needs in the workshop.

- Never use a bent or damaged punch.
- Avoid the use of inferior punches or pieces of scrap rod.
- Grind off any burrs which form on the head of your punches.
- Remember that pin punches are not suitable for use as levers—they will break.

CHISELS

The familiar flat blade, cold chisel is used for cutting and chipping metal and concrete. Applications in the workshop include splitting seized nuts, cutting sheet and thin strip metal and chipping off areas of corrosion. There are other types of chisel for engineering work. Cross-

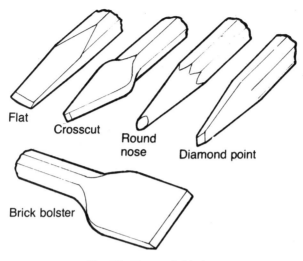

Flat
Crosscut
Round nose
Diamond point
Brick bolster

Fig. 10. Types of chisel

cut chisels are used to cut slots and keyways; round-nose chisels produce slots with a rounded bottom, and diamond-point chisels will cut vee-shaped grooves. Chisels for the building trade include brick-cutting bolsters and heavy-duty flat blade chisels for cutting concrete.

Chisels are made of a good-quality steel or a nickel alloy steel. An advantage of alloy steel chisels is that they can be sharpened with a file when you are working away from the workshop.

Flat blade chisels are made in several sizes with blade widths of 6 mm to 25 mm ($\frac{1}{4}$–1 in) readily available from toolshops. Chisel length increases with the width of its cutting edge and there is a range of handle lengths for each size of chisel. For example, a chisel with a 12 mm cutting edge is made with an overall length of 150, 200, 250 or 300 mm. The other types of chisel are also made in a variety of sizes.

Care of Chisels

A chisel with a mushroom head is dangerous because it is difficult to use a hammer accurately on it and a glancing blow may well produce a chip of flying metal. Always grind off any slight mushrooming as soon as it appears and restore the handle to its original bevel-shaped end. Put all bent, cracked and badly mushroomed chisels on the scrap heap.

A chisel must be sharp; a blunt one will not cut but only act as a wedge, and will probably be ruined by brute force applied by the hammer. Alloy steel chisels should be sharpened with a smooth file to prevent loss of temper in the cutting edge. Carbon steel chisels are usually sharpened on a grindstone and it is important to quench the cutting edge frequently to prevent loss of temper through overheating. A flat blade chisel is tapered towards the cutting edge which should be maintained at an angle of 60° for general work with iron and steel. Brass cuts best with an angle of 50°. The cutting angle is 45° for copper and 30° for aluminium. The blade edge has a slight curve to stop the corners digging into the work.

When the tapered part of a chisel becomes too short through constant resharpening, its working life can be prolonged by reforging the blade. The correct taper can be restored with a grinder but it is better to draw out the blade in a forge. The chisel blade should be brought to red heat and then drawn out to the correct taper with a hammer on an anvil. Once the correct taper has been attained, allow the chisel to cool slowly. The taper can now be given its final reshaping on a grindstone. Before it

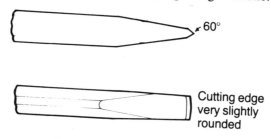

Fig. 11. Chisel sharpening

can be used, the chisel must be hardened. Heat the first 25 mm of the blade to a cherry red colour and then quench it in cold water. Polish the end of the blade ready for the tempering process. Apply heat with a flame torch, at the top of the tapered part of the blade. Watch for the temper colours and when a dark purple colour is seen running down to the cutting edge, the blade should be quenched. With a final trim to the cutting edge, the chisel is ready for use.

Chisel Safety

- Always use the correct chisel for the job. The use of a chisel which is too wide is unsafe and the cutting edge may be damaged.
- Use a firm grip, with the hand about 25 mm below the head. Don't hold it too tightly; if the blade should slip off the work, you may injure your hand.
- Use the correct size of hammer. The striking face of the hammer must always be bigger than the head of the chisel. A small hammer will

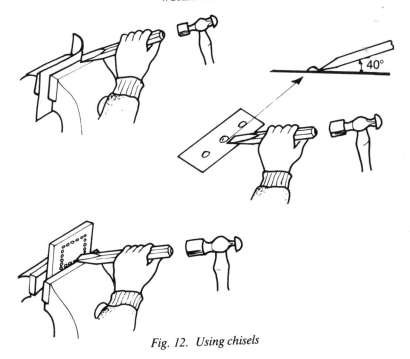

Fig. 12. Using chisels

have little effect and one which is too large can damage both chisel and workpiece. A flat blade chisel with a 12 mm ($\frac{1}{2}$ in) shank requires a 450 gm (1 lb) hammer; an 18 mm shank chisel should be used with a 900 gm hammer.

- Make sure the work is secure, clamping small articles in a vice. Always chisel away from your body. Wear goggles, especially if you are cutting metal or masonry where there is a risk of eye injury from flying chips of material.
- Never use the corner of the cutting edge—it is liable to fracture if the full weight of a hammer is applied to such a small part of the blade.
- Don't strike the side of a chisel which has become jammed. This can result in a broken or cracked blade.
- Never work with bent or damaged chisels and remove mushroom heads as soon as they appear.
- Don't use a chisel as a makeshift lever or crowbar.

Using a Chisel

Sheet and thin metal strip can be cut with a chisel. Clamp the material between the jaws of a vice with the line to be cut level with the top of the jaw faces. The metal can then be cut by chiselling along the top of the vice jaw with the chisel at an angle of about 40° to the vice. Holes or slot can be cut in sheet metal with a chisel. Place the metal on a flat piece o wood to protect the bench top. Cut the slot which has been marked out holding the chisel at an angle to the work.

Rivet heads can be chopped off with a chisel. With the chisel at 40° to the workpiece, the rivet head can soon be removed. Watch out for flying rivet heads, and if you are working in front of a window protect the glass.

Seized nuts are another problem solved with a chisel. Support the underside of the nut with a weight or place it on a solid surface. Cut through the side of the nut with a really sharp chisel. Very often, two or three sharp blows with a hammer and chisel will stretch the nut threads enough to allow the nut to be removed with a spanner (see fig. 82).

FILES

Files are made in a variety of sizes, shapes and grades of cut. The teeth are on the body of a file which has a tang at one end for attaching a wooden or plastic handle. The specification of a particular file depends on:

- **Length**. The size of cutting area, measured from the base of the tang to the end of the file.
- **Type of cut**. There are three types of teeth, or cut, in fairly common use.

Table 2. Grades of file cut

Type	Teeth per inch	Teeth per cm	Use
Dead smooth	70–110	27–43	Gives a polished, precision finish
Smooth	60–65	23–26	Gives a finish to general work
Second cut	28–42	11–16	A general-purpose file; it will remove metal quite quickly but does not give a smooth finish
Bastard	22–32	8–12	Removes a lot of metal quickly; leaves a rough surface
Rough	14–22	5–8	Very coarse cut; a rasp

Single cut files have rows of teeth running diagonally across the file, in one direction only. They are used for cutting hard steel. A farm example of their use is sharpening mower knife sections. This type of file is often called a reaper file.

Double cut files have two rows of teeth. They run diagonally across the body of the file in two directions. This type of file is used for general engineering work.

Rasp—a very coarse file with individually cut teeth. Used for cutting wood and very soft metals.

- **Grade of cut.** This relates to the coarseness or fineness of the teeth. Table 2 gives details of the grades available.

The most useful files for the farm workshop are second cut. Some bastard files will also be needed for heavy work and some smooth cut for obtaining a good finish.

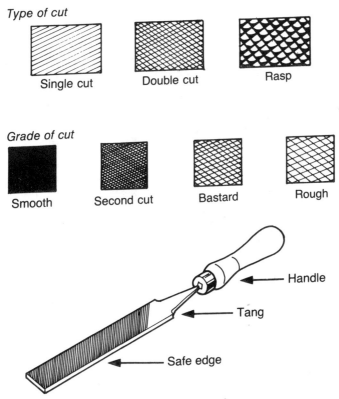

Fig. 13. Files—grades and cuts

Shapes of File

A *Flat file* is used for general work. It is tapered in length and width. The faces have double-cut teeth and the edges are single cut. Typical sizes range from 100 mm long by 13 mm wide up to 350 mm by 35 mm (4 in long by $\frac{1}{2}$ in wide up to 14 in by $1\frac{3}{8}$ in).

Hand files are different from flat files because they are parallel for their entire length. Both faces have double-cut teeth and either one or both edges are single cut. Those with one smooth edge are called safe-edge files. They are used to prevent undercutting when filing out a square corner. Sizes are similar to flat files.

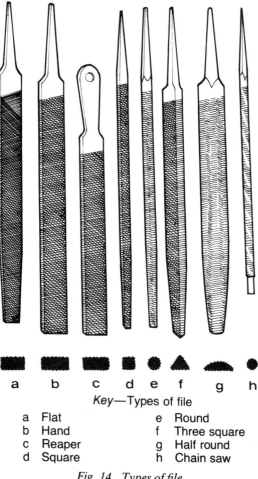

a　b　c　d　e　f　g　h

Key—Types of file

a	Flat	e	Round
b	Hand	f	Three square
c	Reaper	g	Half round
d	Square	h	Chain saw

Fig. 14. Types of file

Reaper files are hand files with single-cut teeth and often have a shaped metal handle. They are used for hard metal, particularly for sharpening cutting edges such as knife sections.

Square files are used for slots, square holes and corners. They have double-cut teeth on all faces and taper for the final third of their length. Typical sizes range from 100 mm long by 4 mm square up to 300 mm by 12 mm (4in by $\frac{5}{32}$ in up to 12 in by $\frac{15}{32}$ in).

A *Round file* is used for opening out holes, rounding inside corners and similar jobs. It tapers for the last third of its length. The larger files usually have double-cut teeth whereas the shorter ones are single cut. Popular sizes range from 100 mm long by 3 mm diameter up to 350 mm by 14 mm.

The *Three-square file* is triangular in section. It is used for filing angles of 60° to 90° and in awkward positions and corners when metal must be removed. The three-square file has double-cut teeth. Typical lengths are from 100 mm to 300 mm.

Half-round files are useful for forming a radius on a piece of metal. The curved face is not a semi-circle. The flat face is double cut and the curved faces of second-cut and smooth files are single cut. The bastard file has double-cut teeth on both faces. Typical sizes are from 100 mm long by 11 mm wide to 350 mm by 34 mm.

The *Rasp* is used for wood, very soft metal and some non-metallic materials. One face is flat and the other curved. Some rasps have a tang.

Besides the common types of file described, there are many special-purpose files including mill files or knife-edge files for saw sharpening; mill files may have rounded edges. The magneto file is a small, fine-tooth file for cleaning contact breaker points. Chain-saw files for sharpening chain-saw teeth are round, parallel files made in various diameters to suit a range of chain teeth. A guide handle is used with the file to ensure accurate tooth shape.

Using Files

Never use a file without a proper handle on the tang. An unprotected tang is dangerous and will cause you to file inaccurately.

File teeth are meant to cut in one direction only. Take a firm grip on the handle with one hand, using the other to support and guide the end of the file. Apply just enough pressure to make the file cut properly. Relax the pressure during the return stroke, raising the file slightly away from the work. Too much pressure on the forward, cutting stroke will make the file rock, producing a rounded surface. Keep the file level with the work when the teeth are cutting. When filing in a vice, make sure the work is secure and that it is at a comfortable height. Take any steps possible to prevent large components moving while they are being filed.

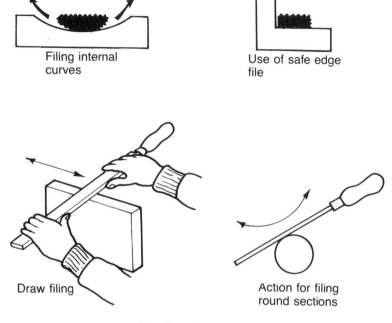

Filing internal curves

Use of safe edge file

Draw filing

Action for filing round sections

Fig. 15. Filing technique

Take up a comfortable stance with your feet apart and try to maintain a steady filing rhythm. Don't work too fast; about sixty strokes per minute is a good filing speed. Files are expensive, so make sure you use all of the teeth.

When filing a shaft or other round material, rock the file in an arc. This prevents the formation of flats on the curved surface. Round and half-round files should be moved around the curved surface of the hole in order to maintain the correct shape. Take great care when filing out a corner. A safe-edge file will prevent you undercutting the vertical edge.

Drawfiling is a useful technique for obtaining a very good finish. A fine-cut file is used, the blade being gripped in both hands and the width of the file drawn back and forth along the work with light pressure. This technique allows the teeth to cut in both directions. Chalk may be rubbed into the teeth to act as a lubricant and improve the surface finish. A polished surface can be obtained by wrapping emery cloth around the file blade and using the drawfiling technique.

Care of Files

Never use a file as a lever, crowbar or hammer. Files are made of very hard steel and are liable to shatter if misused.

Use new files with care and avoid using them on very hard materials as this will destroy the teeth. Use partly worn files for mild steel and save the new ones for tougher work. Use an old file for hot metal.

Clean choked file teeth with a file card. This is a type of wire brush with short, stiff bristles. Any stubborn particles can be removed with a thin strip of soft metal. Don't use a file on oily or greasy surfaces because teeth clogged with grease will not cut—they must be cleaned with a solvent. Chalk rubbed into file teeth will reduce choking, especially when working with soft metals.

File teeth are brittle and for this reason files should be stored in a way which prevents them from rubbing together. Keep them in a rack or wrapped in a cloth roll but never loose in a box or drawer. Don't throw files on to a bench or drop them on the floor; they won't bounce! Keep your files dry—a rusty file is useless. Time spent in careful cleaning and storage will be repaid with longer file life and better results.

HACKSAWS

The hacksaw is a general-purpose saw for cutting metal and other materials. Some hacksaws have adjustable frames suitable for different length blades. Others have fixed frames. There is provision for fitting the blade in line with, or at right-angles to, the frame.

The junior hacksaw is a small, inexpensive saw handy for cutting small-section material and plastics. A padsaw is a simple handle used with a short length of hacksaw blade. It can be used in places where there is insufficient room to work with a proper hacksaw.

Hacksaw Blades

There are variations in length, number of teeth and material used to make hacksaw blades.

- *High-speed all-hard blades* are made from special steel. They will cut quickly and accurately but in unskilled hands there will be frequent breakages because they are brittle. The work must be secure and the blade must not be twisted while the cut is made.
- *High-speed flexible blades* are only hardened on the cutting edge and are unbreakable with normal use. Flexible blades are ideal for general purposes but are less accurate, except in skilled hands.
- *Flexible blades* made of lower quality steel are suitable for the handyman who only needs to cut mild steel and other soft materials.

These somewhat cheaper blades will not cope with hard metals and they are a false economy for the farm workshop.

Blades for hand hacksaws are made in two lengths: 250 mm and 300 mm (10 in and 12 in). They may have 14, 18, 24 or 32 teeth per 25 mm (or inch). The best blade for general work has 24 teeth per 25 mm; blades with 32 teeth per 25 mm are needed for cutting thin material. Always keep two or three teeth in contact with the metal you are cutting. The teeth will be ripped off if a coarse blade is used for thin-section metal.

Table 3. Selection of hacksaw blades

| Material thickness | | Blade—teeth per 25 mm | |
mm	in	Hard material	Soft material
less than 3	less than ⅛	32	32
3–6	⅛–¼	24	24
6–12	¼–½	24	18
over 12	over ½	18	14

As a general guide use a fine blade for thin sections and hard metal; a coarse blade is required for thick sections and soft material. Pipe is an exception. A piece of 25 mm pipe may have a wall thickness of only 2 mm so a fine blade must be used. Table 3 provides a guide to the selection of the correct blade for different materials.

High-speed, flexible blades are best for general work. For very accurate cutting, select an All-Hard blade and use it with care.

Using Hacksaws

The following points should be observed:
- Fit the blade with the teeth pointing away from the handle (a hacksaw cuts on the forward stroke).
- To tension the blade take up the slack and then tighten the wing nut a further two or three turns. Take care—a slack blade will not cut accurately; a blade which is too tight can damage the blade locating pins on the saw frame.
- Clamp the work square in a vice.
- Avoid starting a new cut on a sharp edge or corner and always start the cut with plenty of teeth in contact with the metal.
- It may be helpful to pull the saw back two or three times—guide the blade with your thumb to keep it in the correct position.
- Pressure should be steady on the forward cutting stroke and released on the return stroke. Use only light pressure on thin sections.

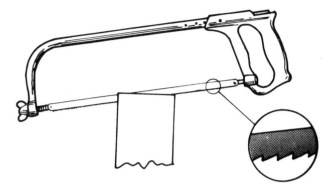

Fig. 16. Using a hacksaw

- Cut with the full length of the blade and at no more than sixty strokes per minute. Reduce the speed for heavy metals.
- Don't allow the blade to bend or twist in the cut.
- Don't use a new blade in a cut started with an old one—this will damage the new blade's teeth. Either complete the cut with another partly worn blade or start cutting from the other side of the metal with a new one.
- When the saw is not in use slacken the blade tension.
- Hang the hacksaw on a peg to prevent frame distortion and to protect the blade.

HAND DRILLS

A small hand drill with a capacity of about 8 mm is a fairly cheap tool which comes in handy on occasions. A larger 13 mm capacity drill will be needed for boring larger holes. With the vast range of power tools available, hand drills have lost their popularity but are still worth having for those jobs which must be done away from a power supply such as drilling holes in masonry in out-of-the-way spots. As they are slow-speed drills, much cheaper drill bits can be used. Sharpening drill bits and using drills are dealt with in Chapter 2.

TINSNIPS

Used for cutting sheet metal, tinsnips are made with straight or cranked blades. They are classified by length, typical sizes ranging from 200 mm to 350 mm (8 in to 14 in).

Straight tinsnips are used for general work and for trimming edges to

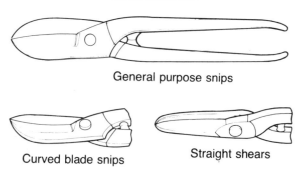

General purpose snips

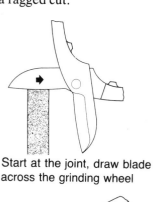

Curved blade snips

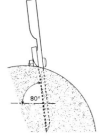

Straight shears

Fig. 17. Tinsnips

the required size. Snips with curved jaws are intended for cutting round corners. When using tinsnips, grip the handles as far as possible from the cutting blades. Keep the blades at right-angles to the material and don't close the cutting jaws completely—this tends to distort the edge and give a ragged cut.

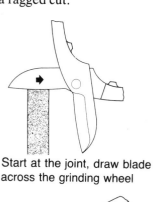

Start at the joint, draw blade across the grinding wheel

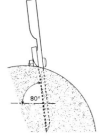

Present cutting edge at 80° to the grinding wheel

Grinding will create a burr; before closing jaw carefully remove the burr on a flat oilstone

Whilst bending downwards the waste should also be forced away from the lower blade to allow an easy passage of the tool through the material

Fig. 18. Sharpening and using tinsnips

The cutting edges of tinsnips must be kept sharp with a fine grit wheel. To sharpen the edges open the jaws as wide as possible and grind the cutting edges to an angle of 80°. Draw the blades lightly across the grinding wheel, taking great care to prevent overheating. Do not grind the inside face of the blade and remove any burr formed during sharpening with an oilstone. Make sure that the pivot bolt is tight at all times and keep the hinge point well lubricated.

The effort of cutting thick or tough material will be reduced if one handle of the tinsnips is held in protected vice jaws.

Waste material should bend downwards when cutting and should be forced away from the lower jaw to allow easy passage of the snips.

In workshops where a lot of sheet metal work is done, a guillotine or shearing machine should be considered.

Take great care when using tinsnips which have a turned end on the handles. They can give the palm of your hand a nasty pinch.

BOLT CUTTERS

Designed for cutting bolts, rod, bar, wire and chain, bolt cutters consist of two heavy-duty cutting jaws operated through a linkage by a pair of handles.

Adjustment is provided to maintain a slight clearance between the blades when cutting round-section metal. The jaws should just meet when used to cut flat sections. There are several sizes of bolt cutter, each with a maximum cutting capacity. If these limits are exceeded, there is a serious risk of damaging the cutting edges. A typical pair of general-purpose bolt cutters, 760 mm (30 in) long, are designed to cut soft steel rods and bolts up to 14 mm diameter and high-tensile steel up to 9 mm diameter.

Check the capacity of bolt cutters before purchase, they are an expensive item so make sure to get a pair which are large enough for your purpose.

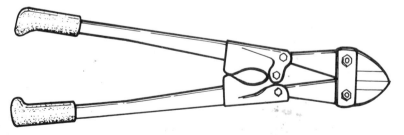

Fig. 19. Bolt cutters

TAPS AND DIES

A *tap* is used to cut a thread in a previously drilled hole. This form of thread is called an internal or female thread. Taps can also be used to restore damaged internal threads.

Taps are usually supplied in sets of three for each size and type of thread. The first is a *taper tap*; it is chamfered for the first eight to ten threads so that the tap can be started in a hole without difficulty. Once the basic thread shape has been made with a taper tap, a *second tap*

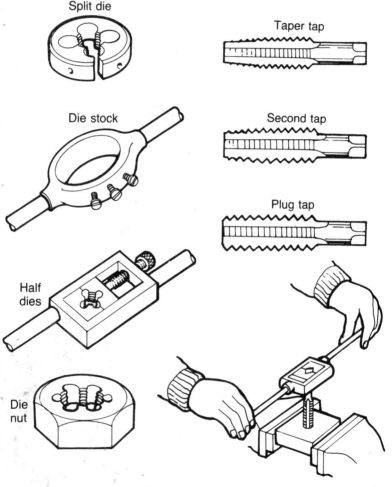

Fig. 20. Taps and dies

is used. This has the first two or three threads chamfered and the remainder cut a full depth of thread. A second tap can be used to complete a thread in a through hole.

A *plug tap* has full-depth cutting teeth from the start and is needed for tapping a blind hole.

Taps have a square end for fixing into a *tap wrench*. This is an adjustable holder suitable for a range of tap sizes. In confined spaces, especially when cleaning out a damaged thread, a spanner can be used to turn a tap.

Dies are used to make external or male threads, one die being required to make a particular size or type of thread. The most common form of die is the *split die* which is held in a special wrench called a *die stock*. Three set screws in the die stock are used to hold a split die in position and to make slight adjustments to the die.

The centre screw is used to open the die slightly when making the first cut. Then the centre screw is slackened a little and the outer screws tightened to increase the cutting depth of the die until the correct thread profile is achieved.

A split die is slightly tapered on one side to help start the die on the rod. It is important to place the die in the diestock with the tapered face downwards. In this position, the information on the die will be visible.

Half-dies consist of two rectangular blocks, each with a half-die on one edge. They are fitted into a die stock which can be adjusted to give the required depth of thread. Half-dies are made in matched pairs.

The *die nut* is similar to a split die but has no split and is hexagonal. It is really intended for cleaning damaged external threads and is turned with a spanner.

There are boxed sets of taps and dies to produce all thread forms and they can also be purchased individually. Many workshops will have little use for taps and dies and in these circumstances it will probably be best to buy a few taps and dies of the common sizes, rather than a comprehensive set. A quality set of metric taps and dies with stocks and handles in a wooden storage box will cost over £100.

Using Taps and Dies

When cutting a thread, always keep the tap, or die, square with the work. Do not exert excessive pressure on the tool or it may break the cutting teeth. Use a lubricant, preferably cutting oil or tallow, when making a thread.

When drilling a hole prior to tapping a thread, it is important to select the correct size of drill bit for the chosen thread rate and diameter. Some examples of tapping drill sizes for the more common thread rates are given in tables 4–7.

Table 4. Tapping drill sizes for BSW and BSF threads

Tap size in	BSW in	mm	Drill size BSF in	mm
$\frac{3}{16}$	$\frac{5}{32}$	4	$\frac{5}{32}$	4
$\frac{1}{4}$	$\frac{13}{64}$	5	$\frac{13}{64}$	5
$\frac{5}{16}$	$\frac{9}{32}$	7	$\frac{9}{32}$	7
$\frac{3}{8}$	$\frac{5}{16}$	8	$\frac{21}{64}$	8
$\frac{7}{16}$	$\frac{23}{64}$	9	$\frac{25}{64}$	10
$\frac{1}{2}$	$\frac{27}{64}$	11	$\frac{7}{16}$	11
$\frac{9}{16}$	$\frac{31}{64}$	12	$\frac{1}{2}$	13
$\frac{5}{8}$	$\frac{17}{32}$	13	$\frac{9}{16}$	14
$\frac{3}{4}$	$\frac{21}{32}$	16	$\frac{43}{64}$	17
$\frac{7}{8}$	$\frac{49}{64}$	19	$\frac{51}{64}$	20
1	$\frac{7}{8}$	22	$\frac{29}{32}$	23

Metric equivalents to nearest full millimetre

The tapping drill sizes may be varied slightly if necessary. For example, where a $\frac{13}{64}$ in drill is not available for tapping a $\frac{1}{4}$ in BSW thread, use the nearest size you have. Both $\frac{3}{16}$ in or $\frac{7}{32}$ in would be suitable.

Once the correct size hole has been drilled, a taper tap should be fitted in a tap wrench. Make sure the work is secure, if possible in a vice. When starting to cut the thread, check that the tap is square with the work. If this is not done, the thread will be out of true. Once the thread is started, the tap should be turned back a little after each half turn or so. This will

Table 5. Tapping drill sizes for UNC and UNF threads

Tap size in	UNC in	mm	Drill size UNF in	mm
$\frac{1}{4}$	$\frac{13}{64}$	5	$\frac{13}{64}$	5
$\frac{5}{16}$	$\frac{9}{32}$	7	$\frac{9}{32}$	7
$\frac{3}{8}$	$\frac{5}{16}$	8	$\frac{5}{16}$	8
$\frac{7}{16}$	$\frac{23}{64}$	9	$\frac{25}{64}$	10
$\frac{1}{2}$	$\frac{27}{64}$	11	$\frac{29}{64}$	12
$\frac{9}{16}$	$\frac{31}{64}$	12	$\frac{33}{64}$	13
$\frac{5}{8}$	$\frac{17}{32}$	13	$\frac{19}{32}$	15
$\frac{3}{4}$	$\frac{41}{64}$	16	$\frac{11}{16}$	17
$\frac{7}{8}$	$\frac{49}{64}$	19	$\frac{51}{64}$	20
1	$\frac{7}{8}$	22	$\frac{29}{32}$	23

Metric equivalents to nearest full millimetre

Table 6. Tapping drill sizes for ISO metric coarse threads

Tap size mm	Drill size nearest whole millimetre	approx in equivalent
6	5	$\frac{13}{64}$
7	6	$\frac{15}{64}$
8	7	$\frac{17}{64}$
9	8	$\frac{5}{16}$
10	9	$\frac{11}{32}$
12	10	$\frac{25}{64}$
14	12	$\frac{15}{32}$
16	14	$\frac{35}{64}$
18	16	$\frac{39}{64}$
20	18	$\frac{11}{16}$
22	20	$\frac{49}{64}$
24	21	$\frac{53}{64}$
27	24	$\frac{15}{16}$
30	27	$1\frac{3}{64}$

keep the tool clean and produce a good-quality thread. When the basic thread shape has been formed with a taper tap repeat the process with a second tap, and in the case of a blind hole it will be necessary to use a plug tap to complete the thread.

It is easier to start a die if the end of the rod is chamfered. Secure the rod in a vice before starting work. Adjust a split die with the centre screw so that it does not take a full depth of cut. Place the die on the chamfered end with the taper die teeth in contact with the rod. Make sure you fit the die correctly in the stock. Check that the die is square with the rod and then start threading. Turn the die backwards at frequent intervals to keep it clear of metal chips. Re-adjust the die to cut the full depth of thread and repeat the process.

Table 7. Tapping drill sizes for BS pipe threads

Tap size in	Drill size in	mm
$\frac{1}{8}$	$\frac{11}{32}$	9
$\frac{1}{4}$	$\frac{15}{32}$	12
$\frac{3}{8}$	$\frac{19}{32}$	15
$\frac{1}{2}$	$\frac{3}{4}$	19
$\frac{3}{4}$	$\frac{31}{32}$	25
1	$1\frac{7}{32}$	31

Care of Taps and Dies

- Remember to use plenty of lubricant when cutting a thread.
- Don't force a tap or die and do turn it back frequently to keep the cutting edges clear.
- After use, taps and dies should be cleaned, wiped with an oiled cloth and stored in a partitioned box. This will protect the cutting edges.

REAMERS

These are rather expensive and most farm mechanics will find little use for them. Reamers are used to enlarge existing holes with great accuracy. An example of their use is cleaning out a plain bush after it has

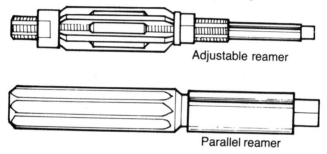

Adjustable reamer

Parallel reamer

Fig. 21. Reamers

been pressed into its housing. This process will return the bush to its correct size.

There are two types of hand reamer. The expanding version can be adjusted within narrow limits to fit different size holes. The less expensive, parallel reamer is designed to fit one size only. Reamers can be purchased in sets or singly. They are used in a similar way to taps and are fitted in a handle similar to a tap wrench. Care must be taken to keep a reamer perfectly square in the hole; it should be turned slowly and excessive pressure should be avoided. Paraffin can be used as a lubricant for cutting brass.

MEASURING TOOLS

Rules

A good-quality steel rule is essential for accurate work. For small jobs a 300 mm / 12 in steel rule is ideal. A 2 m and a 10 m steel tape will be needed for larger projects. Steel rules and tapes will rust if neglected. A light smear of oil will keep them in good condition.

Feeler Gauges

These are used for measuring small clearances between two parts. Typical farm workshop uses include checking spark plug gaps, contact breaker point gaps and valve tappet clearances. Always wipe them clean before use.

Feeler gauges have a number of blades of varying thicknesses. Each blade is marked with its size, either in hundredths of a millimetre or thousandths of an inch. The blades are housed in a metal case which

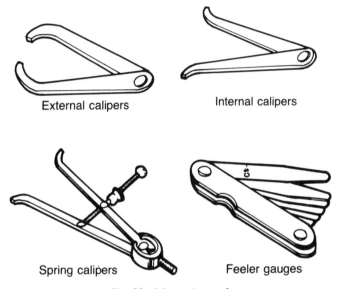

External calipers   Internal calipers

Spring calipers   Feeler gauges

Fig. 22. Measuring tools

protects them when they are folded away and serves as a handle when the gauge is in use. Feeler gauges should be treated with great care to prevent damage. After use, wipe the blade with an oiled cloth to prevent rust.

Calipers

Depending on type, calipers are used with a rule to measure either internal or external dimensions, and their accuracy depends very much on the skill of the user. The cheaper form of caliper has two legs held together by a pivot bolt with a friction washer. Spring calipers are tensioned with a bow spring in the handle and are adjusted with a screw thread.

Internal calipers are used to find the diameter of a hole. The measurement is taken by opening the legs until they reach the maximum dimension of the hole. The calipers should then be rocked backwards and forwards slightly to check that a true reading has been taken.

External calipers are closed until they lightly touch the material without springing the legs. In both cases, the measurement is read off on a rule.

Dividers have straight legs. They are used for transferring measurements or marking circles, using a centre punch dot as the centre of the circle.

THE MICROMETER

Although it is not possible to obtain very accurate dimensions with calipers, micrometers will measure with an accuracy of 0·01 mm or 0·001 in. Even more accurate micrometers are made but would not be used in a farm workshop.

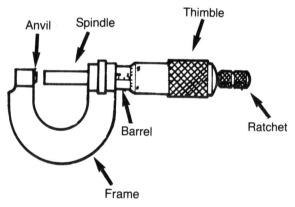

Fig. 23. Micrometer

The three types of micrometer—internal, external and depth models—are made in both metric and imperial versions. Some micrometers have a set of attachments making them suitable for measuring over a wide range of dimensions. Others can only cope with a narrow range, for example 50–75 mm or 2–3 in.

The External Micrometer—Metric

An *external micrometer* consists of a horseshoe-shaped frame with a fixed 'anvil' at one end and an adjustable 'spindle' at the other. The spindle is adjusted by means of a small threaded cylinder called the 'thimble' which turns on a threaded shaft called the 'barrel'. The thread has a pitch of $\frac{1}{2}$ mm so the spindle moves 0·50 mm per revolution. The rim of the thimble is divided into fifty parts. This gives a reading of 0·01 mm for each division on the thimble.

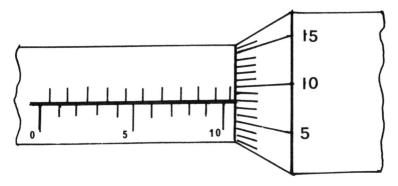

Fig. 24. Reading a metric micrometer

In fig. 24 there are two large 5 mm divisions visible on the barrel which give a reading of 10 mm. One small division is also visible, representing one full turn of the thimble, giving a further 0·50 mm. Finally, the reading on the thimble is 8. This adds 8 × 0·01 mm to the total measurement. The micrometer reading in the diagram can be shown as follows:

Large barrel divisions	2 × 5·00 mm =	10·00 mm
Small barrel divisions	1 × 0·50 mm =	·50 mm
Thimble divisions	8 × 0·01 mm =	·08 mm
	Reading	10·58 mm

The External Micrometer—Imperial

The barrel of an imperial micrometer has 40 threads per inch. The circumference of the thimble has 25 equal divisions. One revolution of the thimble moves the end of the spindle 0·025 in, so in 40 revolutions the spindle will move 1 inch (40 × 0·025 in = 1 in). When the thimble is turned through just one division, the end of the spindle moves a distance of 0·001 in.

The barrel is marked off into 10 divisions, each representing 0·1 in and each of these divisions is subdivided into 4 parts. It will be seen that each one of these sub-divisions represents one revolution of the thimble and is equal to 0·025 in.

In the fig. 25 there are two large divisions visible on the barrel and three subdivisions giving a measurement of $2 \times 0·1$ in plus $3 \times 0·025$ in. The thimble shows a reading of 11 which represents an additional $11 \times 0·01$ in. The micrometer reading in Figure 25 can be shown as follows:

Large divisions on barrel	$2 \times 0·1$ in	$= 0·200$ in
Small divisions on barrel	$3 \times 0·025$ in	$= 0·075$ in
Thimble divisions	$11 \times 0·001$ in	$= 0·011$ in
	Reading	$0·286$ in

Some examples of micrometer readings are given in the questions at the end of the chapter. The best way to learn how to read a micrometer is to follow the above method in the workshop and get someone to check your results.

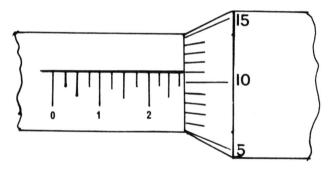

Fig. 25. Reading an imperial micrometer

The Internal Micrometer

This type of micrometer has a measuring unit which works in the same way as an external micrometer. Various extension rods can be fitted to the head, allowing the instrument to be used to take accurate dimensions over a wide range of internal diameters. A common use of an internal micrometer in the larger repair shops is measuring wear in engine cylinders.

Another specialist micrometer is the depth micrometer. An example of its use is to measure the depth of holes and slots.

Care and Use of Micrometers

When taking a measurement with a micrometer, keep the spindle and anvil faces square with the part being measured. Many micrometers have a ratchet drive at the outer end of the spindle which is used to turn the spindle and thimble unit when taking a measurement. The ratchet knob should be turned carefully until it slips, indicating that the measurement has been taken and the reading may be noted.

After use, a micrometer should be wiped carefully and stored in its box. A very light coat of thin oil on the spindle and measuring faces will prevent corrosion.

MARKING TOOLS

Scribers

These are made of hard steel and have a sharp point which is used for drawing lines on metal. If a scriber line is difficult to follow, try rubbing white chalk over the metal before scribing the line. A special dye, called engineer's blue, can be painted on bright metal surfaces before marking out shapes and holes. Engineer's blue is available in both liquid and paste forms.

The centre punch described on page 38 is used for marking the centre point ready for drilling a hole. It also helps to start the drill in the required position.

Letter Punches

Sets of both letter and number punches are useful for marking components during overhaul if there is any doubt about the correct sequence or position of parts during reassembly. This is particularly helpful for the inexperienced mechanic. Letter punches are also useful for marking your hand tools.

Bevels and Squares

There are several types of bevel and square which can be used to achieve accuracy when marking out or checking work. An engineer's *try square* made from good-quality steel is very accurate when new. Careful storage and use are essential to ensure that this accuracy is maintained.

A *combined try square and mitre* can be used as a square in various planes, a 45° bevel and also as a straight edge for checking alignment or trueness of a flat surface. The straight edge also serves as a rule. Some combination sets have a spirit level in the handle.

POWER TOOLS: DRILLS

Every workshop will have at least one electric drill, a small benc'
grinder and perhaps a small portable compressor. There is a wide choic
of power tools available and great care should be taken in selecting th
best models for your purpose.

Most electric drills run on single-phase 240 volt mains; some larg
pedestal drills may require three-phase supply. It is also possible to bu'
electric drills designed to operate on lower voltages giving added safety
but in this case a transformer and low-voltage circuit must be installed i'
the workshop. Compressed-air-driven hand drills are also available.

The factors to consider when selecting a drill are chuck capacity
speeds and available attachments. A small 10 mm ($\frac{3}{8}$ in) capacity drill i'
suitable for light work and a heavy-duty 19 mm capacity model for the
bigger jobs.

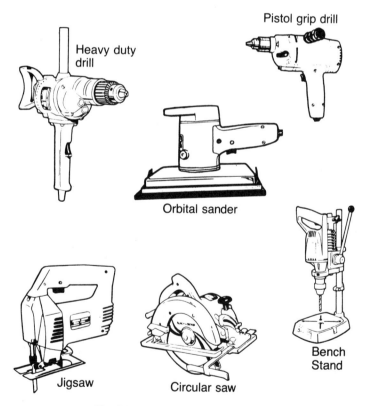

Pistol grip drill

Heavy duty drill

Orbital sander

Jigsaw

Circular saw

Bench Stand

Fig. 26. Electric drills and attachments

Many hand electric drills offer two speeds; others have a choice of four speeds and some have a variable speed control unit. A basic two-speed drill should be adequate for farm work. The lower speed is for masonry and drilling the larger-diameter holes in steel; the high-speed range is suitable for other drilling operations and the use of accessories such as wire brushes and sanders.

Many hand electric drills have a hammer or impact attachment which gives a series of rapid hammer blows to help a masonry drill to penetrate brick and concrete. When hammer drilling, a tungsten carbide masonry bit should be used. The hammer action is engaged with a lever on the drill. It should be noted that not all masonry bits are suitable for hammer drills.

The chuck size of a drill indicates its maximum capacity when drilling steel. Larger holes can be drilled in softer metals and masonry if drill bits with reduced shank diameter are used.

There are many accessories for electric hand drills. These include sanding discs, abrasive cutting wheels, hole saws and wire brushes. Other attachments will convert the drill into a circular saw, jig saw or orbital sander. Many electric hand drills can be fitted in a bench stand.

There is a limit to the size of hole which may be drilled with safety when using a hand-held drill. In larger workshops it will be possible to justify the installation of a bench drill with a chuck capacity of up to 25 mm or an even higher capacity floor-mounted pillar drill. These machines have a variable belt drive or a gearbox which provides a range of drilling speeds and they often have an automatic feed. This means that the downward movement of the drill bit is accurately and automatically controlled to suit the job in hand.

Using Hand Electric Drills

- Make sure the drill bit bottoms in the chuck.
- Tighten it with the key held firmly in position, using all three chuck key holes.
- Secure the work in a vice or with a clamp.
- A centre punch dot mark will help to start the drill bit into work.
- Use the correct drilling speed—fast for most work but slow speed for drilling holes over 5 mm ($\frac{3}{16}$ in) in metal and when drilling masonry.
- Don't force the drill; allow it to work at its own pace.
- Reduce the pressure just before the drill breaks through the metal.
- When drilling thin-section metal, place a wooden block under the work to prevent distortion of the hole when the drill breaks through the metal.
- Larger holes are easier to drill if a small pilot hole is made first.

Table 8. Lubricants for drilling and cutting metal

Metal	Lubricant for drilling and cutting
Steel	Water-soluble cutting oil*
Cast iron	Dry
Copper, brass, phosphor bronze	Dry or paraffin
Aluminium	Paraffin or turpentine

*Water-soluble oil is a white fluid, sometimes called cutting oil, which is mixed with water It has good lubricating and cooling properties.

- Use plenty of lubricant to ensure a clean hole and keep the drill bit cool. The type of lubricant used depends on the material (see table 8).

Twist Drills

Twist drills, or bits, can be purchased in sets or singly. Both high- and low-speed drills are made. The cheaper, low-speed drills are made of carbon steel, have a bright appearance and are only suitable for hand-operated drills. High-speed drills, manufactured from high-speed steel are black in colour and are suitable for power drills.

Metric twist drill sizes increase by steps of 0·1 mm or less. Fractional drill sizes increase in steps of $\frac{1}{64}$ in. A set of metric drills in 1 mm steps and fractional drills in $\frac{1}{32}$ in steps should be adequate for the farm workshop.

Blunt drills will produce badly shaped holes, put excessive loading on the drill motor and waste time. Free-hand drill sharpening is not easy, it is a skill which can be mastered with practice. It is possible to buy a drill-sharpening guide which can be attached to a grinder. Use a medium or fine grit wheel for sharpening twist drills.

For most work, the cutting edges of a drill should be ground to an angle of 59°. In practice, the total angle of the point will be approximately 120°. This also happens to be the angle between two hexagon nuts, placed side by side, as shown in fig. 27d. This provides a simple check for the correct cutting angle. It is important to sharpen the drill so that both the cutting edges are the same length; the point must be central and the web must not be too thin (see figs. 27a and 27c). The drill will not cut unless it has a correct lip clearance angle which should be between 10° and 12°. Aluminium and other soft metals will cut better if the lip clearance angle is increased to 15°. It may help if you study a new twist drill and then copy its shape when you sharpen a blunt one.

Only light pressure should be applied when grinding a twist drill. Either grind under a full flow of cutting lubricant or dry. Continuous quenching can cause tiny cracks in the cutting edges.

Bench and pillar drills have a chuck suitable for parallel shank twist drills. The larger size drills have taper shanks which are fitted into the main spindle of the drill. These shanks have Morse tapers in a range of sizes from No. 1 to No. 6, of which 1 to 3 are in common use. Taper No. 4 is used on drills of about 32 mm diameter; the two largest sizes are used for even bigger twist drills.

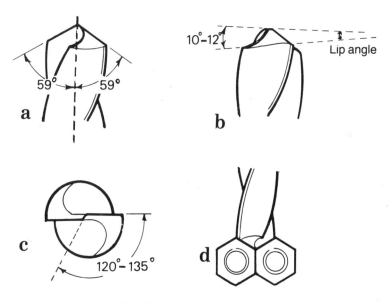

Fig. 27. Sharpening twist drills

GRINDERS

An essential tool in the farm workshop, the grinder is used for sharpening tools, blades and knives and for preparing metal for welding and other processes.

There are grinders for both bench and floor mounting. For most workshops, a 150 mm or a 200 mm (6 in or 8 in) bench grinder will be adequate. (Bench grinders can also be fitted to a pedestal.) Grinders with both single- or three-phase motors are made and where heavy loading is likely, a three-phase grinder is to be preferred if suitable power is available.

Grinders usually have two abrasive wheels, one coarse for general work, the other fine for tool sharpening. A wire brush or polishing wheel can be fitted in place of a grinding wheel if required.

Abrasive Wheels Regulations

Grinding machines fitted with abrasive wheels running at high speeds present considerable hazards to all users. A few sensible precautions

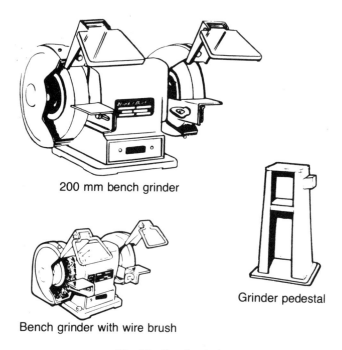

200 mm bench grinder

Grinder pedestal

Bench grinder with wire brush

Fig. 28.   Bench grinders

will reduce the risk of injury caused by sparks or by flying fragments if an abrasive wheel bursts. It is important that the wheel is properly fitted by a person who has been trained and is competent to carry out this task.

The *Abrasive Wheels Regulations 1970*, now covered within the *Health and Safety at Work Regulations 1974*, require that there should be adequate guarding, that abrasive wheels be marked with their maximum permissible speed and that people who mount the wheels receive suitable training. These regulations do not apply to domestic or diy users but will concern all employers of labour.

The following notes will serve as a guide to the requirements. You must refer to the Regulations for their exact detail.

- No abrasive wheel may be operated at a speed in excess of the maximum safe speed marked on the wheel. The grinder must also be marked with its maximum spindle speed.
- The wheel must be a free fit but not loose on the spindle. It should be checked for soundness and brushed clean before it is mounted on to the spindle.
- Both flanges which secure the wheel must be at least one-third of the diameter of the abrasive wheel. The flanges must both be the same size, free from burrs and true. Paper washers should be placed between the flanges and the wheel. The washers must be slightly larger in diameter than the flanges. Check the wheels, washers and flanges for cleanliness before assembly. The clamping nut should be tightened sufficiently to hold the wheel firmly. Hand pressure with an ordinary spanner will be sufficient.
- Guards should be fitted properly. The guards are designed and constructed so that as far as is reasonably practical, they will contain every part of an abrasive wheel if it should fracture during use.
- The work rest should be set as close as possible to the wheel. After adjustment, rotate the wheel by hand to ensure that it can turn freely. The rests should be of a design which does not wrap round the sides of the abrasive wheel. Lack of adjustment can result in serious accidents caused by the work becoming jammed between the rest and the wheel.
- New wheels should be run light for a short while. Keep all people well clear during this test period.

Safe Use of Grinders

- The area around a grinder should be kept clear at all times. The floor must not be allowed to become uneven or slippery.
- Never use a grinder without the guards in place and keep the work rest adjusted to compensate for wear on the abrasive wheel.
- Grinding on the side of the wheel is dangerous, especially if heavy or sudden pressure is applied.
- Eye protection is essential. Many grinders have transparent spark guards above the wheels—keep them in place and in good condition. Use goggles where no spark guard is provided and it is a sensible precaution to wear goggles even if the machine is fitted with a spark guard.
- Don't wear loose clothing when using a grinder, or any other power tool. Belts, sleeves and scarves are easily drawn into a rotating wheel. Never hold the work with a piece of rag while it is being ground.

- Don't stop an abrasive wheel by holding a piece of metal against it. Allow the wheel to come to rest in its own time.
- From time to time the grinding edge will become uneven or scored; it should then be restored to its correct shape with a wheel dresser. One type of dresser has a set of revolving cutters which are held against the grinder wheel. The cutters are very hard and soon restore the surface. Full eye protection must be worn while dressing an abrasive wheel.
- Don't grind very soft metal, such as aluminium. It will clog the wheel surface very quickly.

Types of Abrasive Wheel

There are many types of abrasive wheel with a wide range of specifications. The British Standard marking code which is used for identification gives the specifications in the following order.

0 'Type of abrasive'. An optional prefix code which the manufacturer selects.

1 'Nature of abrasive'. Either aluminium oxide (A) or silicon carbide (C) is used as an abrasive.

2 'Grain size' refers to the size of the grains of the abrasive material and is sometimes referred to as the grit size. A range of numbers is used to indicate grain size. 8 to 24 are coarse, 30 to 60 are medium, 70 to 180 are fine and 220 to 600 are very fine. Only a few numbers are used within any of the grain-size groups.

3 'Grade' indicates the type of bonding material which holds the abrasive material in the wheel. The full alphabet is used to classify the grade. Wheels graded A are soft and Z are hard.

4 'Structure'. This refers to the density of the abrasive material in the wheel. The range is from 0 which is a very dense structure to 14 which is a very open structure. Numbers higher than 14 might be used.

5 'Bond type' means the bonding material used to construct the wheel. The materials used are as follows: V—Vitrified; B—Resinoid; R—Rubber; E—Shellac; S— Silicate.

6 'Maker's mark'. The last part of the code is another optional mark in figures or letters chosen by the manufacturer.

The other important information which must be given is the maximum permissible speed of the abrasive wheel.

An example of an abrasive wheel code is 'A 46 Q 5 V 30W. Maximum permitted speed 4460 rpm'. This indicates that the abrasive wheel is constructed as follows.

0	1	2	3	4	5	6
—	A	46	Q	5	V	30W
Not given	Abrasive— aluminium oxide	Grain size medium	Grade medium hard	Structure fairly dense	Bond vitrified	Maker's own coding

Portable Grinders

The angle grinder is similar in construction to a heavy-duty electric drill but instead of a chuck there is a grinding disc at right angles to the motor drive shaft. Angle grinders can be used on machinery or very large pieces of metal. In this case it is the grinder that is taken to the work rather than the work to the grinder. There are small, lightweight models suitable for jobs such as trimming up metal, removing areas of corrosion and sharpening mower blades. A sanding attachment can also be used with the smaller type of angle grinder.

A typical range of heavy-duty angle grinders has abrasive wheels with a diameter of 180 mm or 230 mm (7 in or 9 in). These power tools are suitable for heavy-duty grinding, trimming and dressing (cleaning) welds, etc. Angle grinders can also be fitted with cutting discs which are suitable for cutting tubing, sheet metal and other materials.

Straight portable grinders are also made; a typical model has a 125 mm wheel and is useful for working on machinery and fabrication work.

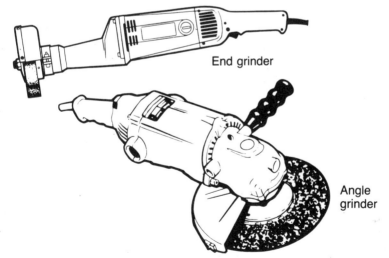

End grinder

Angle grinder

Fig. 29. Portable grinders

Safe Use of Portable Grinders

- Always wear goggles when using a portable grinder. Make sure that the sparks are directed away from any others who are working close by.
- Never use a portable grinder without the guards in place. Make sure that the abrasive wheel or cutting disc is in good condition and fitted correctly.
- Take a firm grip on the grinder before switching it on. Make sure the cable is well away from the grinding or cutting disc. Don't apply excessive pressure to the grinder. When in use, the grinding disc should be at an angle of 30° to 45° to the work.

POWER HACKSAWS

A useful tool in the farm workshop where a lot of fabrication work is done, the power hacksaw will cut through thicker sections of material with greater precision than is possible with any oxy-acetylene cutter.

The basic power hacksaw has a single-speed belt drive from an electric motor. An automatic mechanism disconnects the drive to the saw when the metal has been cut, allowing the user to carry on with other work while sawing is in progress. More expensive models have a choice of sawing speeds and some have a built-in coolant system.

The blades are made from All-Hard high-speed steel or a flexible high-speed cutting steel. They are wider, longer and tougher than those for hand saws. Power saw blades are very expensive too. The pitch of the teeth is much greater because there is little point in using a power saw for material under a thickness of 13 mm. Blades are made with 4, 6, 10 or 14 teeth per inch (or 25 mm). Choose a blade which has at least three teeth in contact with the metal—a coarse blade for soft metals and a finer one for hard materials.

The design of vice which holds the material while it is cut varies with cost and model of saw. The best choice is a vice with two movable jaws which also swivel. If both jaws can be moved along the frame full use may be made of the saw blade so that fewer of those expensive teeth will be wasted. The swivel allows accurate cuts to be made at any angle.

Care and Use of Power Hacksaws

- The sliding part of the saw frame must be well lubricated. The drive belt tension should be checked at regular intervals and adjusted if necessary.

- To ensure efficient cutting and long blade life, the work must be clamped securely in the vice. Fit the blade with the teeth pointing forward on the cutting stroke, the direction of which will vary with make of machine because some cut on the forward stroke, others on the return.
- Set the saw in motion before the frame and blade are lowered on to the work. The saw frame should be supported for the first few cutting strokes. When sawing thinner-section material clamp a number of pieces together in the vice and cut them all at the same time.
- A coolant such as soluble cutting oil should be used, except when sawing cast iron and high nickel chrome steel.
- Help ensure a long blade life by using the correct blade tension, avoiding starting a cut on a sharp corner and not using a new blade in an old cut—turn the work over and start from the other side with the new blade.

SHEARING MACHINES

The shearing machine or guillotine is used for cutting thin sections of metal. It consists of a shear blade, operated by a long handle, which cuts against a fixed blade. The guillotine is bolted to a frame or heavy bench, which in turn must be secured to a wall or floor. A simple model will cut sheet, strip and round metal, capacity depending on size. A typical medium-size guillotine will cut 5 mm sheet, 6 mm strip and 12 mm round bar. Shearing machines for other sections, such as angle iron can also be obtained.

It is most important to keep the blades adjusted; too wide a clearance will produce very poor work.

Plenty of access should be allowed when installing a guillotine, and for safety a piece of chain should be hooked round the handle when the tool is out of use. The handle would give a very nasty knock if it accidentally fell forward.

EXTENSION CABLES

Where possible avoid the use of extension cables which are always a source of danger when they trail across a workshop floor. Plenty of well-positioned wall sockets should reduce the need for them but where there is no alternative use a purpose-made extension. There are a number of reel-type extension cables on the market, some of which automatically rewind themselves after use.

- Avoid leaving a reel-type cable extension with the power switched on when it is not in use. It is liable to overheat and damage cable insulation.
- Check all extension cables frequently. Any damaged cable should be scrapped as soon as it is discovered. For added safety use unbreakable rubberised plugs on all portable power tools.

GENERAL WORKSHOP EQUIPMENT: COMPRESSORS

Most air compressors used on farms will be portable and driven either by an electric motor or a small petrol engine. The compressor is a valuable piece of workshop equipment which will inflate tyres, operate a paint sprayer, blow dirt away from machines and clean spark plugs. Compressed air can also be used to drive power tools.

A *portable* compressor with a maximum air pressure of 8 bar (230 psi) should meet most needs of the farm. Whereas most portable compressors do not have an air receiver tank or storage tank, *fixed* compressors may have either vertical or horizontal air receiver or storage tanks. They are suitable for the larger workshops which will have a permanent airline installed to provide air take-off points in all parts of the workshop.

When using compressed-air equipment, take care to direct the air away from yourself. When cleaning off dust, goggles will prevent dirt getting into your eyes.

BATTERY CHARGERS

A small trickle charger in the workshop will keep tractor and other batteries in a well-charged state during periods when the equipment is not in use. A unit with a charging rate of 2 or 3 amps will be sufficient to maintain in a satisfactory state of charge those battieries which are in storage between seasons. It will also pep up a tractor battery which is left on charge overnight. Some trickle chargers can be adjusted to charge 2, 6 or 12 volt batteries.

Also made are chargers with higher charging rates which will be very useful on the larger farms where a lot of battery charging is required.

It should be remembered that a discharged battery will freeze if it is not protected from frost. The best protection is to keep all batteries well charged during the winter months.

Using a Battery Charger

Before being connected to a charger the top of the battery should be clean and dry. The terminals should be free from corrosion and the battery cells topped up with distilled water. The level of electrolyte should be just above the plates. Batteries with automatic fill should have distilled water poured in until the bottom of the trough is covered. The filler caps should not be tightened, otherwise there will be a pressure build-up when hydrogen and oxygen given off during the charging process are unable to escape. However, auto-fill batteries are usually charged with the cover in place.

Never check a battery with a match or other naked flame as a means of illumination if the charger is situated in a dark corner. The result of mixing oxygen and hydrogen with a flame will be explosive!

The charger can now be connected to the battery. Attach the negative charger clip to the negative terminal and the positive clip to the positive terminal. Check that the charger is set to suit the battery voltage where this applies and then plug into the mains. When all is ready, the current can be turned on. An ammeter on the charger will indicate the rate of charge.

Testing Batteries

The state of charge of a battery can be checked with a hydrometer. It measures the specific gravity of the electrolyte (sulphuric acid) which is directly related to the state of charge. Weak acid indicates a low state of charge.

After a few hours on charge, progress should be checked with the hydrometer. With a cell cap removed, the rubber tube at the bottom of the hydrometer is placed into a cell. Some electrolyte can be drawn into

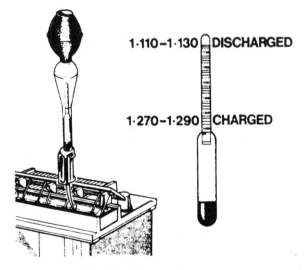

1·110–1·130 DISCHARGED

1·270–1·290 CHARGED

Fig. 30. Using a hydrometer

the hydrometer by squeezing the rubber bulb at the top and then slowly releasing it. Take up enough electrolyte to allow the float to rise from the bottom.

The float has a scale of specific gravity readings marked on it. The figure on this scale which is level with the top of the liquid is the specific gravity. Return the liquid to the cell and then check at least two more cells. Don't let any of the electrolyte drip on to your clothes or skin while taking the reading. It is an acid and will burn. After use, rinse the hydrometer with water.

Table 9. Specific gravity of battery electrolyte

Specific gravity	State of charge
1·270–1·290	Full charge
1·200	Half charged
1·110–1·130	Discharged

Some hydrometers have a float with three coloured bands rather than figures. One colour indicates the battery is discharged, the next is for half-charged and the third is for full charge.

LIFTING TACKLE

Jacks are basic workshop equipment. There are hydraulic or bottle jacks, screw jacks and trolley jacks. The *screw jack* is the simplest type, worked by a handle which operates a threaded lifting unit. It is not suitable for lifting heavy vehicles.

The *hydraulic jack* has an oil reservoir which needs an occasional check for level. Oil is pumped from the reservoir to a lift cylinder through a non-return valve when the handle is operated. The jack is lowered by using the handle to open the non-return valve which releases the oil from the lift cylinder. There are many sizes of hydraulic jack, a typical range having lifting capacities from 2 to 35 tonnes. A 5 to 8 tonne jack should meet most needs in the farm workshop.

Trolley jacks are more expensive but have the extra advantage of allowing movement of equipment after it has been lifted clear of the ground. Lifting capacities of trolley jacks range from 1½ to 20 tonnes or more. The handle is used to pump oil from the reservoir to the lift cylinder. A release lever on the handle opens a non-return valve which allows the oil to flow back to the reservoir when the jack is lowered. Some trolley jacks have a safety lock in the handle, removing the risk of someone letting the jack down accidentally. A foot pedal, which allows rapid raising of the jack when it is not under load, is sometimes provided.

Using Jacks

- Never work under a jacked-up vehicle except when it is also supported with axle stands or sound wooden blocks. An axle stand should be used as an extra precaution even when removing a wheel to repair a puncture. If the jack slips, or someone accidentally lowers the jack, you may have quite a problem on your hands. For extra safety, chock the vehicle wheels before lifting it clear of the ground. When removing a wheel, remember to slacken the wheel nuts slightly before jacking up.
- Always keep hydraulic jacks upright. If the jack is not tall enough, even with the extension screw fully undone, use a sound wooden block to increase the height of the jack. Don't use bricks or a concrete block, they may crumble or slip.

Cranes

There are a number of floor cranes operated with either a wire rope and winch or a hydraulically operated lifting cylinder. A typical workshop model has a lifting capacity of one tonne. The jib can be extended to increase the reach of the crane but in this position the lift capacity is reduced to half a tonne. This is an expensive piece of equipment and can only be justified in workshops where engine removal and similar work is done on a regular basis.

Some workshops have pulley blocks supported from a suitable steel beam. There are special regulations about installing this type of lifting tackle and advice must be sought from the Safety Inspector before the work is put in hand.

The other source of lifting capacity on the farm is the tractor loader or fork-lift truck. Either of these machines, with plenty of rear counterbalance weight in the case of a tractor loader, will be able to deal with the occasional lifting job in the workshop. Purpose-made chain or nylon rope slings should be used for lifting. Check their condition often and scrap any which are damaged.

VICES

All workshops have vices suitable for metalwork. Special-purpose vices for woodwork, pipework and for fixing to pillar or bench drill work tables are also made. Vice size is denoted by the jaw width, a typical range being from 65 mm to 205 mm ($2\frac{1}{2}$ in to 8 in). For general-purpose work a vice with 125 mm or 150 mm jaws will be needed. Some metalwork vices have a quick-release handle. A trigger lever is pressed, allowing the jaws to be opened or closed rapidly. Final tightening of the jaws is done in the usual way.

An old-fashioned leg vice, fixed to the leg of a heavy bench, is very useful for rough or heavy work. Such a vice can sometimes be bought at farm sales. There are several types of special-purpose vice: some have a swivel base, others are portable and can be clamped to a bench or even a tractor drawbar with a single clamp nut.

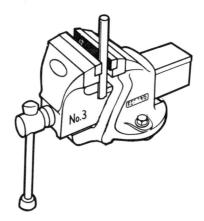

Fig. 31. Metalwork vice

Fitting a Vice

A vice should be bolted firmly to a bench or, if used away from the workshop, to a stand. It may be an advantage to fit a metal plate on the underside of the bench to give added strength to the fixture. The bolts holding the vice should also pass through the strengthening plate.

The height of the vice should allow the user to work in comfort. When installed, the vice jaws should be at elbow height, as shown in fig. 32. The back jaw plate must be far enough forward to allow long material to be gripped in a vertical position.

Care and Use of a Vice

- Working parts should be oiled occasionally. Open the jaws and apply oil to the main screw at the handle end, the main screw thread and nut, and also to the quick-release mechanism, if fitted. Finally, the vice jaws should be closed to ensure even distribution of the oil.

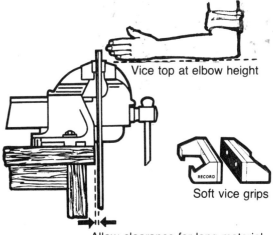

Vice top at elbow height

Soft vice grips

Allow clearance for long material

Fig. 32. Fitting a vice to a bench

- The jaw plates are made of very hard steel; in time they may become chipped and should then be replaced.
- The work should be gripped securely in position. Failure to do this may result in damage to the work and injury to the operator. Use fibre vice grips when holding soft or polished material in the vice.
- Don't use the slide part of the vice as an anvil. Never extend the length of the handle or strike it with a hammer.
- Don't bend or straighten a part when it is held horizontally in a vice, a practice which can result in broken vice jaws. Grip the part in an upright position for this type of work.
- It is advisable to keep an old vice for rough work and for holding parts which are to be welded. This type of work will damage a vice, especially if it is a small or light-duty model.

PULLERS

Pulleys, gears, bearings and similar parts usually need to be a tight fit on a shaft. They can cause problems when a machine is being dismantled for overhaul, a job for the wheel or hub puller. A basic puller has two, or three, hooked legs with a threaded rod. These parts are attached to a hub assembly.

The legs are hooked over the part to be removed and the thread is then tightened against the end of the shaft. As the thread is tightened, the part should gradually slide off. The task is easier if the shaft is clean, free from burrs and well oiled.

Busier workshops may be able to justify the purchase of a puller set. This consists of a puller unit together with several sets of legs which are of different lengths and shapes. Pullers often have a small hydraulic ram in place of the thread. It is operated with a spanner and applies pressure to the shaft so that the component is gradually pulled off.

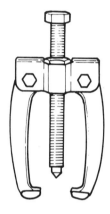

Fig. 33. Hub puller

LUBRICATION EQUIPMENT

A good lever-operated grease gun and some pressure oil cans are the minimum requirements for every workshop. Lever-operated units with a flexible pipe can be obtained for direct attachment to a keg of grease, cutting out the frequent and somewhat messy job of filling grease guns. During filling it is important to prevent the formation of air pockets in a grease gun, and afterwards both oil cans and grease guns should be wiped clean.

Always clean any dirt from grease nipples and oil points before applying the lubricant. This will ensure that dirt will not be carried into the bearing by the oil or grease. Surplus lubricant should be wiped off when oiling or greasing is completed.

A large-capacity oil can, or syringe, can prove useful when filling small gearboxes or bearing housings in very awkward places. Some plastic packs of oil are supplied with a flexible spout for this purpose.

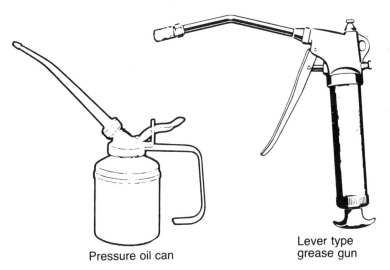

Pressure oil can

Lever type
grease gun

Fig. 34. Lubrication equipment

SPECIAL TOOLS

There are many tools designed for a specific job, particularly for overhaul of tractors and the more complicated machines such as combines and balers. These tools will be required by the machinery dealer but can rarely be justified on the farm.

The tools considered in this chapter have all been of a general nature. Other tools for specific processes or work are dealt with where appropriate in the following chapters.

THINGS TO DO

1. Learn the different spanner sizes well enough to be able to select a particular size at the first attempt. It may help to colour code your spanners by putting a spot of paint on each one. Use different colours for metric, BSW/BSF and A/F spanners.
2. Practise sharpening chisels and screwdrivers. Take care to keep the chisel blade cool.
3. Sharpen some blunt twist drills; use a new one as a pattern, and then test your work by drilling some holes.
4. Learn to recognise the different types of file and always fit a handle on a file tang before you use the file.

5. Always wear goggles when using a grinder. Make sure any sparks you produce with a portable grinder are directed away from any other person in the workshop at the time.

QUESTIONS

1. Why is a coarse hacksaw blade unsuitable for cutting a piece of steel tube 12 mm in diameter? Which is the correct blade for this job?
2. State the specific gravity reading for a battery which is fully charged.
3. What is the correct cutting angle for the point of a twist drill?
4. How should the work rest be set in relation to the abrasive wheel on a bench grinder?
5. What are the readings on the two micrometer barrels shown in fig. 35?

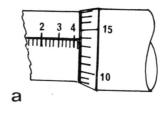

a

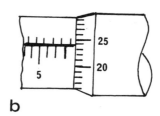

b

Fig. 35. Test micrometer readings

Chapter 3

The Workshop Stores

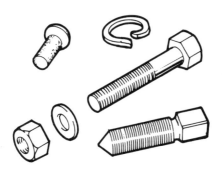

ALL WORKSHOPS must have a well-stocked store with an orderly arrangement of parts and small items of hardware to save time at busy periods. The contents of the store will depend on the work undertaken, size of storage area and distance from the farm to the local service agent. As hundreds of thousands of pounds worth of spares are kept by all tractor and machinery dealers, stocks of implement spares on the farm should be kept to a minimum. It is probably wise to limit these items to fast-moving parts such as filters, fan belts and soil-wearing parts for ploughs and other implements. Most workshops have spares which have accumulated over the years, the bulk of which will never be used, have little value and take up useful storage space.

There are many essential small items, best kept in bins or boxes, which must be part of every workshop store. Nuts, bolts, washers, rivets, keys and split pins are typical examples. Add to these a supply of lubricants, a range of electrical fittings such as plugs, bulb holders and cable, some water supply items including taps, piping, tap washers, and ball valve parts.

Recording shortages is important too. A pencil and notebook seem to disappear when needed, so a sheet of paper on a wall with a pencil firmly secured to a piece of string is a more permanent way of ensuring that notes can be made and read.

NUTS AND BOLTS

The wide range of nuts and bolts together with the many thread types found on farm implements and equipment makes a comprehensive stock of nuts and bolts both difficult and expensive to maintain. The second-hand bolt box holds the solution to many problems!

Bolts, Studs and Set Screws

Hexagon bolts are so well known, they need no description. The hexagon head allows for just one-twelfth of a turn with a ring spanner in confined spaces when slackening or tightening a nut or bolt.

Carriage bolts have a domed head with a square section below. These are used to hold timber on to a metal framework; trailer sides are an example. They are also handy in places where a hexagon head causes an obstruction. In this case the holes in the machine components are square. The carriage bolt head is held in the square and cannot turn when the nut is tightened.

Carriage bolts are difficult to undo when badly rusted and it is sometimes impossible to remove them with a spanner. In this case a cold chisel must be used to split the nut.

It may help to cut a screwdriver slot in the head of the carriage bolt. A screwdriver is then used to stop the head turning. This idea is also useful for holding the heads of hexagon bolts in inaccessible places.

Machine screws are threaded right up to the head. They are made in small sizes only—up to about 6 mm or $\frac{1}{4}$ in diameter. BA threads for electrical equipment will also be found on machine screws. The heads may be round, countersunk, cheesehead etc. Hexagon or square nuts are used. The head may have a screwdriver slot or a cross-shaped slot for Phillips or Posidrive screwdrivers. Sometimes the head has a hexagonal recess for use with an Allen key.

Set screws are similar to bolts but have thread right up to the head. They are used to lock pulleys, gears or collars on to a shaft and to adjust moving parts to suit varying conditions. The head may be hexagonal, slotted, recessed for an Allen key or have a small square head.

Grub screws are very small set screws, threaded for their entire length and often have a tapered point. The head may have a slot or recess for an Allen key. Grub screws are used for jobs such as locking small pulleys on to a shaft. The point on the grub screw is used to help locate the component in the correct position on the shaft.

Plough bolts are special headed bolts for various uses on ploughs and many other machines. The head is usually countersunk so that it does not protrude above the surface of such parts as a mouldboard or share. A small lug or square section below the countersunk face stops the bolt

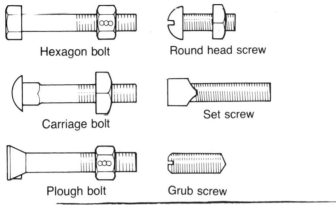

Fig. 36. Types of bolt

from turning while the nut is tightened. Some plough bolts have left-hand threads.

Studs are headless bolts with a thread at both ends. One end is screwed into a threaded hole, the part is placed on the stud and a nut is used to secure the part in position. Cylinder head studs—screwed into the cylinder block—with nuts to hold the head in position is a typical example of the use of studs. A special tool for fitting and removing studs is made. A pair of adjustable grips or the use of two nuts locked together on the upper thread and turned with a spanner are alternative ways of fitting studs.

Self-tapping screws are used for sheet metalwork. After drilling a hole in both of the parts, a self-tapping screw can be used to join them. The hole must be smaller than the screw. The hardened thread on the screw cuts its own thread in the holes.

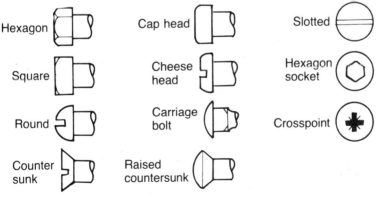

Fig. 37. Bolt and screw heads

Nuts

Hexagon nuts are very commonly used. A few square nuts will be found on older machines.

Wing nuts can be tightened with the fingers. They are useful where frequent adjustments are needed and for securing guards on machinery.

A castellated nut combined with a split pin is used to lock a nut on a bolt. A hole in the bolt is lined up with slots in opposite faces of the nut. A split pin is placed through the slots and hole to prevent movement of the nut. Slackening the nut to align the holes should be avoided if possible. There are different patterns of castellated nut, sometimes known as castle or slotted nuts. A familiar example of the use of a castellated nut is for the adjustment of front wheel bearings on a tractor.

Locking nuts are sometimes used to prevent a nut coming loose. They are thinner than ordinary nuts. When movement takes place between the components bolted together, the thin nut should be put on the bolt before the thick one. The thin nut should be tightened up towards the thick nut by undoing it slightly. The practice of putting the thin nut on top is often due to lack of a suitable spanner to fit the locking nut, but when no movement is required between the components, the thin nut should be on top.

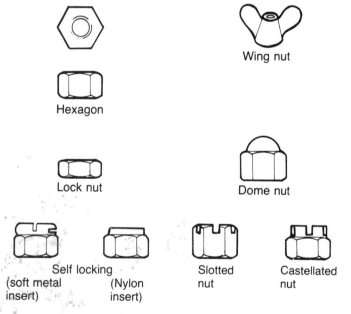

Fig. 38. Types of nut

Self-locking nuts have a soft metal or plastic insert built into the top of the nut. The hole through the centre of the insert is slightly smaller than the bolt thread. As the nut is tightened, the bolt cuts a thread in the soft material. This locks the nut on to the bolt. Another type of self-locking nut has slots cut part way down the centre of each flat. The parts between the flats are bent inwards slightly. When the nut is tightened, the nut grips firmly on to the bolt. Self-locking nuts should only be used once.

Dome nuts are enclosed at the top. They are used to keep corrosion from threads or for applications when a chromium-plated dome nut gives a better finish.

Care of Nuts and Bolts

When replacing damaged or missing nuts and bolts, make sure that the replacement is not only the correct size but also has the correct length of thread. A nut should run freely on to a bolt for at least the full thickness of the nut. Failure to do this may be because the thread is dirty or damaged or the nut has the wrong thread. Make sure that the threads are clean and lightly oiled before assembly. Damaged threads can be restored with taps and dies or with a thread file. A useful way to free a tight thread is to smear it with valve-grinding paste, then turn the nut backwards and forwards. Wash off all traces of paste before final assembly.

Avoid hitting bolt threads with a hammer. A bolt seized in a hole is best removed by slackening off the nut a few turns until it is level with the bolt. A sharp blow with a hammer on the nut should loosen the bolt without damaging the thread.

Threads

Almost all threads are right-handed. When facing a nut, it is tightened by turning it in a clockwise direction. Sometimes a left-hand thread is needed, especially when the rotation of the part secured would cause a right-hand thread to unscrew.

There are two basic thread forms—coarse and fine. The coarse thread is stronger but has a tendency to come loose if subjected to excessive vibration. A fine thread will keep tight but the thinner thread profile (shape) reduces its strength. This can result in a stripped thread if it is tightened carelessly. For this reason, a stud screwed into a casting or soft metal usually has a coarse thread.

Although there are only two basic threads, coarse and fine rates, there are a number of threads in common use. They have differences in pitch and thread profile.

Thread Types

British Standard Whitworth (BSW) and *British Standard Fine (BSF)* are the coarse and fine threads used on many of the older British-made machines. Spanners for these nuts and bolts are marked with the diameter of the bolt to indicate size.

American National Coarse and *American National Fine* threads are used on machinery of American origin. Spanners for these bolts have sizes marked on them relating to the width across the flats of the nuts. This is shown as *A/F*.

Unified National Coarse (UNC) and *Unified National Fine (UNF)* are more recently developed threads which were introduced to provide a common thread in both America and Great Britain. These bolts have a special mark (see fig. 36).

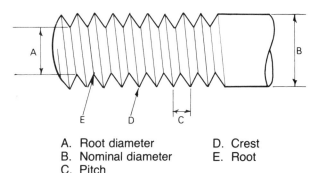

A. Root diameter   D. Crest
B. Nominal diameter   E. Root
C. Pitch

Fig. 39. Dimensions of a thread

Metric threads have been used on Continental machinery for many years and are now standard threads on British equipment. Metric spanners are marked with the distance across the flats of the nuts in millimetres.

British Association thread *(BA)* is a very fine thread rate for small-diameter nuts and bolts, used mainly for electrical equipment. The spanners are marked with a BA size. The most common sizes are from 0 BA (6 mm diameter) to 10 BA (1·7 mm diameter).

British Standard Pipe thread *(BSP)* is used for pipework and is sometimes called gas thread. The size is related to the nominal pipe bore diameter. Some pipe fittings have metric threads.

The pitch of a thread is the distance from the peak of one thread to the peak of the next. To find the pitch of a metric thread, measure the distance between ten threads in millimetres, then divide this length by ten. A bolt with ten threads in 15 mm has a pitch of 1·5. The pitch of imperial threads is found in a similar way: measure the distance, in inches, between ten threads then divide the length by ten to find the pitch.

The various imperial threads have different root diameters. For this reason, two bolts can have the same nominal diameter and pitch but have a different thread profile (shape). This is why a nut may fit one bolt exactly but will not fit another of the same diameter.

Thread Identification

Bolts can be identified with a thread identification chart. First count the number of threads per inch and measure the nominal diameter. Find these figures on a thread chart to complete the identification. Metric bolts are marked with an *M* on the head and measurements should be made in millimetres. A thread gauge can also be used to identify threads. This tool looks rather like feeler gauges but the blades have saw-tooth edges which exactly fit a certain size and pattern of thread. Each blade has its size marked on it. Taps and dies are another useful aid to thread identification. A die should run freely down a bolt if it is the same thread type. The same applies to a nut when checked with a tap. (See tables 10–12, pages 88–9.)

High-Tensile Bolts and Nuts

For many applications, nuts and bolts made of mild steel will be quite adequate. There are other uses, such as engines, where better-quality nuts and bolts are essential. They will be made of high-tensile steel, an alloy steel which has been specially heat treated to give added toughness. High-tensile bolts will have markings on the bolt head which will distinguish them from mild steel bolts.

Machines such as balers and ploughs will often have safety shear bolts which are designed to break if overloaded. Shear bolts are an important safety mechanism and they must only be replaced with the correct type of bolt.

Different manufacturers use a variety of markings to indicate the grade of bolts and nuts. When renewing high-tensile nuts and bolts, it is important to make sure they are replaced with bolts of the same grade.

This is most essential when reviewing safety shear bolts. Some typical tensile grade markings on bolt heads include the letters *S*, *T* and *R*.

Locking Devices

Some locking devices prevent bolts from coming loose, others only reduce the risk of this happening. A castellated nut and split pin, a thin lock nut used with a standard size nut and a self-locking nut are

Table 10a. Identifying Whitworth and BSF threads

Diameter in	Threads per inch		Width across spanner jaws	
	BSW	BSF	early BSW in	BSW/BSF in
$\frac{1}{4}$	20	26	·525	·445
$\frac{5}{16}$	18	22	·600	·525
$\frac{3}{8}$	16	20	·710	·600
$\frac{7}{16}$	14	18	·820	·710
$\frac{1}{2}$	12	16	·920	·820
$\frac{9}{16}$	12	16	1·010	·920
$\frac{5}{8}$	11	14	1·100	1·010
$\frac{3}{4}$	10	12	1·300	1·200
$\frac{7}{8}$	9	11	1·480	1·300
1	8	10	1·670	1·480

Table 10b. Unified threads

Diameter in	Threads per inch		A/F spanner size (normal series)
	UNC	UNF	
$\frac{1}{4}$	20	28	$\frac{7}{16}$
$\frac{5}{16}$	18	24	$\frac{1}{2}$
$\frac{3}{8}$	16	24	$\frac{9}{16}$
$\frac{7}{16}$	14	20	$\frac{5}{8}$
$\frac{1}{2}$	13	20	$\frac{3}{4}$
$\frac{9}{16}$	12	18	$\frac{13}{16}$
$\frac{5}{8}$	11	18	$\frac{15}{16}$
$\frac{3}{4}$	10	16	$1\frac{1}{8}$
$\frac{7}{8}$	9	14	$1\frac{5}{16}$
1	8	12	$1\frac{1}{2}$

Note. The original Whitworth bolts had a larger head than the same diameter bolt with BSF thread. A later British Standard provided for both Whitworth and BSF to have the same size head for each thread diameter.

The A/F spanner sizes given for Unified threads refer to the standard bolts. There are some variations in spanner size for the heavier range of bolts.

Table 11. Metric threads

Diameter mm	6	8	10	12	14	16	18	20	22	24
Pitch mm	1·0	1·25	1·5	1·75	2·0	2·0	2·5	2·5	2·5	3·0
Spanner size mm (across flats)	10	13	17	19	22	24	27	30	32	36

Metric bolts are stamped with the letter 'M'. The chart refers to a coarse rate of thread.

Table 12. Pipe threads (BSP)

Pipe bore in	$\frac{1}{8}$	$\frac{1}{4}$	$\frac{1}{2}$	$\frac{3}{4}$	1	$1\frac{1}{2}$
External pipe diameter in	$\frac{13}{32}$	$\frac{17}{32}$	$\frac{27}{32}$	$1\frac{1}{16}$	$1\frac{3}{8}$	$1\frac{29}{32}$
Threads per inch	28	19	14	14	11	11

BSP is used for water pipe and also for grease nipple threads on many machines.

Table 13. British Association Thread (BA)

Size	Diameter mm	in	Pitch mm	Threads per inch
0	6	·236	1	25
1	5·3	·209	0·90	28
2	4·7	·185	0·81	31
3	4·1	·161	0·73	35
4	3·6	·141	0·66	38
5	3·2	·126	0·59	43
6	2·8	·110	0·53	48
7	2·5	·098	0·48	53
8	2·2	·087	0·43	59
9	1·9	·075	0·39	65
10	1·7	·067	0·35	72

Note. There are smaller sizes of BA bolt. For example 14BA is 1 mm in diameter and 20 BA is just 0·48 mm diameter.

examples of permanent locking devices. Spring washers and star washers will stop a nut coming loose under normal circumstances.

A *Spring Washer* is a very simple locking device. It is a split ring of spring steel which, when compressed by a nut, still exerts upward pressure to hold the nut in position. Spring washers are generally used more than once but must be discarded when they become flattened with age or use.

Star Washers or *Shakeproof Washers* are thin, flat washers with a serrated edge. They should only be used once because when the serrations have been flattened the washer will no longer lock.

Tab Washers and *Locking Plates* have many uses, including engine construction. After tightening the nut or bolt, the washer tabs or corners of the locking plate are prised upwards and tapped round the nut or bolt head. Some tab washers have an internal tab which fits into a keyway. These are used to lock a nut on a shaft.

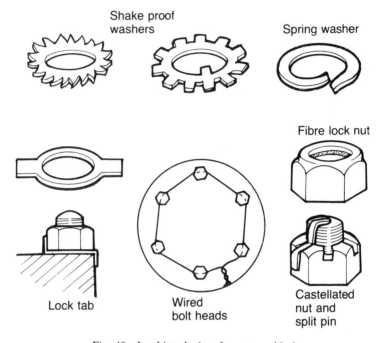

Fig. 40. Locking devices for nuts and bolts

Locking Wire can be used by threading it through small holes drilled in the head of one or more bolts. When all the heads are linked with wire, it is twisted and the bolts cannot turn.

Adhesives are another form of locking device. A special preparation is smeared on to the threads before assembly. When set, the adhesive holds the nut in position. Firm pressure with the spanner will release the seal.

RIVETS

No workshop stores is complete without a good selection of rivets. They are made of soft iron, copper, brass and other metals. Rivet size is measured by the diameter of the shank, usually referred to as its gauge. Rivets for fixing sections to a combine harvester knife are generally 5 gauge or 6 gauge.

A rivet provides a method of permanently joining two pieces of metal, often a piece of sheet metal on to a thicker framework. They can

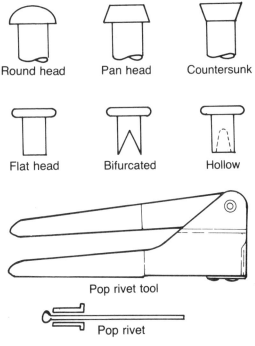

Fig. 41. Types of rivet

also be used for a moving joint such as on a blacksmith's tongs. There are several types of rivet; some of the more important ones are as follows.

Round Head or *Snap Head* rivets are used for general-purpose jobs. The head protrudes above the surface of the work. Knife-section rivets are frequently this type.

Countersunk rivets are used when a flush surface finish is required. Heads with different countersink angles are made to suit various thicknesses of metal.

Pan Head rivets are similar to round head and are used for general work.

Flat Head rivets are used to join two pieces of very thin metal. They are also called Tinman's rivets.

Bifurcated rivets are suitable for joining thin metals, canvas etc. They have two tails which are bent over and hammered tight after assembly of the components. Bifurcated rivets are made of soft, non-ferrous metals.

Hollow rivets are used to fix brake and clutch linings. They are made of brass or copper.

Pop Rivets were developed for the aircraft industry but are now in common use. They are very useful for joining two pieces of metal where only one side is accessible. A Pop rivet consists of a soft hollow rivet with a steel pin through the centre. A special rivet gun is used to pull the pin up through the hollow section. This movement continues until the rivet has swelled and the steel pin snaps or pops.

KEYS AND PINS

Gears, pulleys and levers can be secured in position on a shaft with keys or pins. A key is used to fix a component in an exact position, especially where correct assembly of parts is important. Engine timing gears are an example. A keyway is cut into the shaft and the hub to accommodate the key.

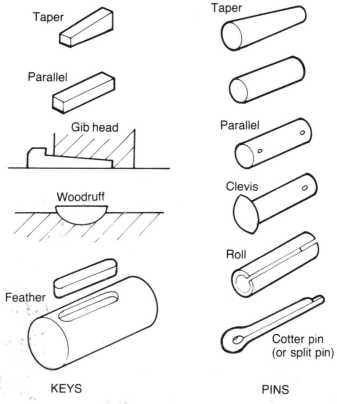

Fig. 42. Keys and pins

The more common types of key include the following:

- *Parallel key.* May have square or rectangular section. It is parallel for its entire length.
- *Feather key.* A special type of parallel key, often secured to the shaft with small countersunk screws. The key is a sliding fit in the other keyway, which allows the part to move along the shaft. A feather key is sometimes used as part of the engagement mechanism for simple drive arrangements.
- *Taper key.* Although parallel in width, the thickness tapers slightly. A taper key is driven firmly into both keyways, giving secure attachment of the component to the shaft. A taper key can often be removed by driving the keyed component further on to the shaft. This should loosen the key.

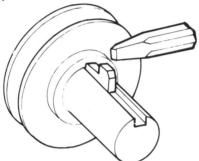

Fig. 43. Removing a gib head key

- *Gib head key.* A taper key with a head, which is used to withdraw the key. Gib head keys are used where pulleys must be removed from time to time.
- *Woodruff key.* A halfmoon-shaped key which fits into a semi-circular slot in a shaft. It is useful on tapered shafts because the extra depth of the keyway helps keep the key in position, especially during assembly. The deep key slot tends to weaken small-diameter shafts. To remove a woodruff key from a shaft first tap one end into the keyway to rotate the key in it. The key can then be extracted with a pair of pliers.

Splined and *serrated shafts* or *hubs* provide a positive method of connecting a component to a shaft. The splines transmit drive from one part to the other and also allow parts to be moved along the shaft. A gearbox is a good example of the use of a splined shaft. The splines transmit drive and are used to slide gears in and out of mesh.

A serrated shaft has a number of splines or serrations, sometimes with one large master spline to ensure correct assembly of parts. Serrated shafts are used in most tractor steering linkages.

Pins of various types are used to secure parts to a shaft. There are several different types.

- *Taper pin.* A round, slightly tapered steel pin driven through holes in a hub and shaft until it is tight.
- *Parallel pins.* Sometimes driven through holes in the hub and shaft until tight. The pin will have a small taper to start it in the hole and will be a very close fit. Another type of parallel pin has a hole in each end for split pins which hold it in place. A clevis pin is also parallel but with a head at one end and a split pin hole at the other.
- *Roll pins* or *hollow pins* are made of spring steel. They are tubular with a slit along the full length and a taper at one end to start the pin in the hole. Pressure on the pin in the hole reduces its diameter slightly causing it to grip very firmly in the hole.
- *Split pins* (sometimes called *cotter pins*) are an essential stores item. A box of assorted split pins will provide most of the sizes likely to be needed and also make a useful storage tray. Most split pins have one leg slightly longer than the other, making the pins easier to open. They are generally made of steel, but brass is used where corrosion presents a problem.

WASHERS

Spring washers and star washers are described under locking devices. The workshop stores will need a good selection of spring washers and flat washers. They spread the pressure of a bolt head or nut and should always be used when working with wood and thin metal. Flat washers provide packing material under a nut when the bolt is too long and can be used to take up wear on shafts, etc. Most flat washers are made of bright mild steel and some are made of cheaper, black mild steel. A range of sizes to fit common bolt diameters can be bought in boxes of assorted washers. A supply of large-diameter washers which have various thicknesses and widths is very useful for taking up wear on axles and shafts of machinery. Include some large-diameter washers with small holes, they are handy for holding guards in position.

GASKETS AND SEALS

Repairs to engines, gearboxes and other components often require new gaskets or seals during reassembly. Single gaskets and kits can be purchased from machinery agents but there will be occasions when it will be quicker to make a gasket in the workshop.

Cylinder head and engine manifold gaskets are made of copper,

copper and asbestos or other soft metals. These must be purchased. Heat-resisting gasket material, suitable for exhaust gaskets, is available in sheet form.

Many gaskets are made of gasket paper or cork. Both of these materials are sold in sheets of varying thickness. It is not difficult to cut a gasket using a small ball-pein hammer or a sharp craft knife. Thick brown paper can be used to cut a temporary gasket.

Sealing compounds in tubes or tins can be used with a gasket to ensure a good joint. Both setting and non-setting sealants are available. As well as making a good joint, the sealant also holds the gasket in position during assembly. Ordinary lubricating grease, or the thicker water pump grease, will help hold gaskets in position but are not very effective seals.

Washers made of fibre and soft metals such as copper are also used as seals. A box of assorted fibre washers should be in the workshop store. The washers will be useful for stopping leaks from fuel pipe connections, oil drain plugs, etc. Copper washers are used to seal diesel fuel injectors in the cylinder head. They should be replaced, or the old ones annealed, when fitting service exchange injectors. Some spare injector washers and a few sparking plug washers are useful items to keep in stock.

OTHER SMALL ITEMS

Circlips

These are split rings made of spring steel which expand inwards or outwards, depending on type. They are used to hold circular components on a shaft or in a housing. Circlips are used to retain the needle bearings in a power take-off shaft universal joint.

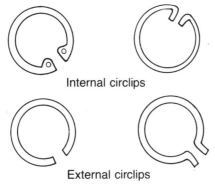

Internal circlips

External circlips

Fig. 44. Types of circlip

External circlips are fitted in a groove around the circumference of a shaft, retaining components in the proper position. Internal circlips are placed in a groove inside a housing to hold such items as bearings in place.

Grease Nipples

Grease nipples are made in a variety of types and sizes. Some are threaded, others are a very tight push-fit. It is possible to buy a boxed assortment of grease nipples.

Nails

These will be required for odd repair jobs. There are dozens of different sorts. A supply of round-head wire nails, oval heads, panel pins, clouts for fixing roofing felt and galvanised roofing nails for corrugated iron and asbestos should meet most needs. Nails are made in various lengths according to type. Round-head wire nails are from $\frac{1}{2}$ in to 6 in long.

Woodscrews

These are usually made of mild steel or brass. The heads may be round, countersunk or raised countersunk with a slot, or recess for a crosspoint type screwdriver. Screws are classified by their gauge and length. The gauge number relates to the diameter of the screw shank, the number increases with size.

To find the size of a screw, use a screw gauge. This is a thin metal or plastic plate with slots cut in the sides. The different width slots are the same as common screw gauge diameters. A screw's gauge can also be found with a simple calculation. Measure the head diameter in sixteenths of an inch. Double the number of sixteenths and then subtract two. This gives the gauge. For example, an 8 gauge screw has a head diameter of $\frac{5}{16}$ in. Double the 5 to get 10 then subtract 2 which gives 8 gauge.

Screw gauges range from 0000 to 50; the common sizes are 4 to 12. A pilot hole must be drilled before putting a screw into timber. Drill bits are available which make a clearance hole for the shank and a smaller hole for the thread in the same operation.

Wire

Coils of thin and medium diameter, galvanised mild steel wire should be kept in the store. The size of wire is ordered by its diameter in mm or SWG number. The Imperial Standard Wire Gauge is the British measure for wire and sheet metal but the metric equivalent sizes are now in common use.

Table 14. Wire and sheet metal sizes

SWG	Inches	mm	SWG	Inches	mm
0	·324	8·2	14	·080	2·0
5	·212	5·4	16	·064	1·6
6	·192	4·9	18	·048	1·2
8	·160	4·1	20	·036	0·9
10	·128	3·2	22	·028	0·7
12	·104	2·6	24	·022	0·6

Imperial Standard Wire Gauge sizes start at 000000 and end at 40 (0·464 in to 0·0048 in). Table 14 gives some examples from the middle of the SWG range.

Pipes and Unions

The farm workshop will be concerned with repairs to pipes for fuel, water and oil, including hydraulic systems. There are many types of union, pipe and clip in use. Fittings for farm water supply are considered in Chapter 7.

Like many other items of small hardware, boxes of assorted fuel and oil pipe fittings are readily available. These provide for most basic needs.

Engine cooling system parts are normally connected with flexible rubber hose, often in a pre-formed shape. Some spare lengths of the common size of hosepipe, together with a selection of hoseclips should be kept in store.

Small diameter plastic tubing is often used for fuel systems, especially for small petrol engines. The fitting of new plastic pipe can be simplified by softening the ends in warm water.

Hydraulic pipes for trailers and other implements work at very high pressures. New hose ends must be fitted properly which is usually a task for the dealer who will have the proper tools for the job. Certain types of hose end can be replaced in the farm workshop without the use of expensive special tools.

Ordering Spares

An almost endless list of small hardware could be included here. The more common parts have been described in this chapter. Obtaining these items will cause few problems, other than their cost. Parts for tractors and machinery need much more attention to detail. Give the storeman as much information as possible. Model and serial number are essential facts, so when a part has a number marked on it, use it. When

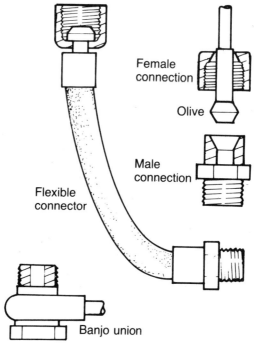

Female
connection

Olive

Male
connection

Flexible
connector

Banjo union

Fig. 45. Fuel pipe unions

there is more than one number, it pays to use all of them. Parts not made by the tractor or implement manufacturer, such as bearings, can cause problems. It is best to take the old unit as a pattern because the numbers on the bearing may not be the ones used in the parts catalogue.

It is a good idea to keep a record book with the details of model and serial numbers for all machines on the farm. Make a note of the details when the new machine is delivered. Identification plates sometimes get lost!

THINGS TO DO

1. Look for the different types of nut and bolt.
2. Try to identify the various thread types. Use any of the methods given in this chapter.
3. Find as many of the different locking devices listed in this chapter as you can on tractors and machinery at a farm you know.

4. Search for the different types of key, circlip and rivet. The workshop store will be a good place to start.
5. Measure some wood screws and calculate their gauge.

QUESTIONS

1. Name five types of bolt head in common use.
2. What is the difference between a bolt and a stud?
3. How can Metric and Unified bolts be recognised without checking thread rates?
4. Explain what is meant by the pitch of a thread.
5. List four materials suitable for making gaskets.

Chapter 4

Materials in the Farm Workshop

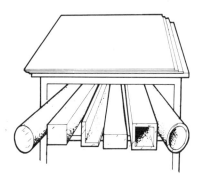

MANY MATERIALS, both metals and non-metals, will be found in the farm workshop. Some of them are in common use and a small stock of such materials are an essential part of the workshop stores. These include various sections of mild steel such as sheet, rounds, flat strip and angle iron; also a small quantity of copper, brass and timber.

METALS: FERROUS

Metals are divided into two groups—ferrous and non-ferrous. Metal containing iron is classed as a ferrous metal. Where small proportions of other metals are mixed with the iron, the material is known as a ferrous alloy. All ferrous metals contain a small proportion of carbon which has an important effect on what type of ferrous metal is produced.

Non-ferrous metals contain no iron. There are many non-ferrous metals but few are used to make or repair farm machinery and equipment. Non-ferrous alloys which are a mixture of two or more metals other than iron (such as brass and solder) will also be found in the workshop.

Iron ore, mined in many parts of the world, is placed in a blast furnace with measured amounts of coke and limestone. The limestone acts as a flux which combines with impurities in the ore to form slag. Molten iron is drawn off from the blast furnace and run into sand moulds called pig beds. The resulting slabs of iron are known as pig iron, the raw material used to produce various types of iron and steel.

Cast Iron

Pig iron, coke and limestone are put into a special furnace called a cupola. The pig iron is refined in the cupola and the molten metal is then drawn off into ladles for transport to the casting shop. Here, ready-made sand moulds are filled with the molten metal. This makes it possible to produce items of intricate shape quickly and relatively cheaply. When cool, the new casting is removed for cleaning before it is taken to the machine shop. Cast iron contains from 3 to 4 per cent carbon and very small amounts of silicon, sulphur, manganese and phosphorus. The actual amounts vary according to the type of cast iron produced. When the molten iron is allowed to cool normally, the metal is known as grey cast iron. If the molten metal is cooled quickly the iron has a finer structure which is harder than grey cast iron. This form of iron is called white cast iron.

When molten, cast iron is very fluid and can be used to make quite intricate castings such as cylinder heads and cylinder blocks for engines. It has many other uses around the farm including wheel weights for tractors, rib roll rings and gearbox housings of machinery.

Grey cast iron is easy to machine and drill. Holes are usually drilled in cast iron without any lubricant. Cast iron can be welded without great difficulty, both with electric and oxy-acetylene equipment. Care must be taken when welding to prevent rapid cooling of the repaired item as this may result in cracking. Larger items are pre-heated before welding to reduce the risk of cracking.

Cast iron is a brittle material but has considerable strength in compression; it resists crushing.

Chilled Cast Iron

This is white cast iron. Either the whole casting or parts of it can be chilled to give hard-wearing qualities to certain parts of the casting. A chilled cast-iron ploughshare is an example of the part-chilled technique. A metal chilling plate is placed in the bottom of the sand mould when making such a ploughshare. This plate causes rapid cooling of the molten metal while the upper surface cools more slowly, producing a share with a hard-wearing underside and a softer top. This type of share is self-sharpening as the softer top wears away at a faster rate than the

FARM WORKSHOP

base. Cast-iron shares are less popular now; many farmers prefe
longer-lasting non-brittle steel shares.

Malleable Castings

Cast iron is a brittle material. Where an intricately shaped item is
required as part of a machine but is subject to shock loads, cast iron i
not suitable. However, if the casting is given special heat treatment—i
is cooled very slowly to anneal or soften it—the resulting componen
will stand shock loads without fracture. Malleable iron can be hammered or bent. The process of making malleable castings is expensive
and steel is often used as an alternative. Examples of use include cutte
bar fingers on some harvesting machinery and plough parts such as disc
coulter brackets.

Malleable iron has all the advantages of cast iron but has greate
strength and is not brittle. It is easy to machine but difficult to weld. It
can be brazed.

Wrought Iron

This type of ferrous metal is not used in the manufacture of farm
machinery. It is almost pure iron with only about 0·1 per cent carbon.
You may still find the odd shackle or timber wedge made of wrought
iron in the farm workshop. This material gives warning of breakage:
instead of suddenly snapping, it will stretch with the outer surface
peeling away to reveal a slate-like structure. Wrought iron is still used
by ornamental blacksmiths to make very expensive gates and other
ironwork.

STEEL

Steel has a much lower carbon content than iron, the amount varying
from 0·1 to 1·5 per cent. Steel becomes harder and more brittle as the
carbon content increases. It is produced from pig iron, with large slabs
of red-hot steel passed through rolling mills to reduce it to the required
size and shape.

Mild Steel

This is the cheapest and most commonly used type of steel around the
farm. It is also known as low-carbon steel and as this name suggests, it
contains only 0·1 to 0·3 per cent carbon. Mild steel can be machined,
drilled, bent, sawn and welded with ease. It has no great strength and
rusts quickly if not protected from the weather.

Mild steel is available in many different sections including rounds, flats, angles, tube and sheet. It is readily available from metal merchants and many ironmongers' shops.

There are various ways of reducing or preventing the effects of rust on mild steel. Short-term remedies include paint, rust-preventing fluids and even waste oil or grease. More permanent protection is possible by coating sheet mild steel with plastic and this material is sometimes used for cladding or roofing farm buildings as well as plastic-coated chain-link fencing. Another way of preventing corrosion is to apply a thin coating of zinc to the steel to galvanise the metal. A rather expensive method is to coat steel with a very thin layer of tin, producing tin plate.

Low-carbon steel cannot be hardened by heat treatment methods used for better quality steels. However, it is possible to case-harden mild steel (see page 106).

Uses of mild steel include guards on many farm machines, tractor bonnets, fuel tanks, farm gates, most of the sheet metal found on farm machinery and galvanised water tanks.

Medium-Carbon Steel

Although more expensive, medium-carbon steel is harder and tougher than mild steel. It contains between 0·3 and 0·7 per cent carbon and can be welded and forged. Medium-carbon steel can also be sawn, drilled and machined but as this material has greater strength, it is easier to work with if the steel is annealed (softened) by heat treatment. After machining is completed, the metal is rehardened and tempered before use.

Uses of medium-carbon steel include plough beams, plough discs, axles, implement frames, cultivator tines, etc.

High-Carbon Steel

Carbon content varies from 0·7 to 1·4 per cent and this type of steel tends to be brittle. It is also known as cast steel or tool steel. Cold chisels, punches and wood chisels are examples of the use of carbon steel with a carbon content of up to 1 per cent. Steel with a higher carbon content is used to make such items as taps and dies for thread cutting, high-speed twist drills and files.

Alloy Steels

An alloy steel is made by adding one or more non-ferrous metals to steel. There are many different types of alloy steel.

By adding *tungsten* and *chromium* to steel, a high-speed cutting steel is produced. This is used to make high-quality metalworking tools including twist drills, taps and dies.

Stainless steel is an alloy steel widely used in the dairy industry and has also replaced much of the chromium-plated steel used in car manufacture. It contains more than 10 per cent chromium and for some applications, nickel is added too.

Nickel added to steel gives a metal which can be heat treated to give very hard wearing properties. Nickel steel is particularly suited to the production of case-hardened shafts and gears.

HEAT TREATMENT OF STEEL

Heat treatment is a term used to describe a number of different processes which change the properties of metal. All carbon steels can be heat treated but the processes suitable for mild steel are very limited.

When dealing with small items, it is possible to carry out many of the heat treatment processes in the farm workshop.

Hardening gives the metal a tough, hard-wearing property.

Tempering is necessary after hardening, because most metals become rather brittle after the hardening process. Tempering relieves internal stresses which cause brittleness.

Annealing is a process which makes the metal soft and easy to work.

Case Hardening gives a hard outer surface with a shock-resisting, softer centre.

Hardening and Tempering

Steel containing more than 0·3 per cent carbon can be hardened by heating it to red heat and then quenching it in cold water. Factory processes may use brine—salt water—or oil for quenching (cooling). The quench gives a hard metal which may also be brittle; for this reason, hardening is followed by tempering.

Apply heat here and watch colours
run to cutting edge

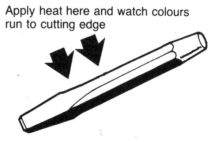

Fig. 46. Tempering a cold chisel

Metal is tempered by being reheated to a definite temperature and then quenched. The colour of polished steel changes as the temperature increases, giving an accurate guide to the temperature of the metal. The temper colour changes from the natural colour of steel to straw, red, brown, purple and blue.

A familiar, but undesirable, example of hardening steel is when a screwdriver is sharpened with a grindstone without proper cooling. The blade overheats, turns blue and is very brittle. When used in this condition the corner of the blade soon snaps off. To remove the brittleness, the screwdriver blade should be heated to a dark purple colour and then quenched. The colours will be easy to see if the blade is polished with emery cloth before starting to heat it. The heat should be applied a little way up the shank of the screwdriver and the temper colours will then be seen running down towards the tip. As soon as the dark purple colour appears, the screwdriver must be quenched at once. Plunge it vertically into the water.

To save all this work it is much better, of course, to sharpen a screwdriver with a file. However, this is the method for tempering any item made of carbon steel. A cold chisel, drawn out in a forge and sharpened on a grindstone would be tempered, after hardening, by the same method.

Table 15. Temper colours and temperatures

Colour	Temperature °C	Example of article or tool
Pale straw	230	Scrapers and scribers
Dark straw	240	Twist drills
Yellow-brown	250	Punches
Purple-brown	260	Plane irons, rivet snaps
Purple	270	Axes
Dark purple	280	Screwdrivers, cold chisels
Dark blue	300	Springs

Annealing

A process used to soften metals and make machining or cold working easier. Steel is annealed by bringing it to red heat and then allowing it to cool very slowly; other metals are annealed by slightly different treatment. Carbon steels require annealing before work can be done with them and when other metals, such as copper, become hardened with age or by being worked or hammered, these, too, can be restored to their softer state by annealing.

Case Hardening

This heat treatment process gives a wear-resistant outer surface with a softer, shock-resisting centre for such items as ball bearings, gudgeon pins and gear wheels. Carbon steels above 0·3 per cent carbon can be case hardened by a factory process. The same process of heating steel and quenching it under carefully controlled conditions is also used to harden small areas of a component. For example, a shaft on a harvesting machine may need hardness or toughness on one section only. This can be heat treated after machining processes are completed, keeping the cost of the shaft to a minimum. Care should be taken to avoid heating such items when carrying out repairs.

Low-carbon steel cannot be case hardened by the process outlined above. It can only be case hardened by adding carbon to the surface layers of the metal, a process which is easily carried out in the farm workshop. The component is heated to a bright red and then dipped in a carbon-rich powder. The item is then reheated to the same bright red colour, causing the surface layer to absorb some of the carbon. Heating and dipping is repeated two or three times to achieve the required depth of hardness.

The depth of hardness can be tested with a file and, if not satisfactory, the process is repeated. The case-hardening powder can be purchased from most toolshops. This process is also known as carburising.

IDENTIFYING TYPES OF IRON AND STEEL

Although there are a number of tests which may be used to find the exact identity of a piece of iron or steel, the exact content of steel, especially alloy steels, cannot be found by simple farm workshop trials. However, the farm mechanic can distinguish between the basic ferrous metals with the following simple tests.

1. Appearance

The basic types of iron and steel are easy to identify by their colour and surface texture. Cast iron has a grey, granular surface, casting lines are sometimes visible and very often the part will have a raised number which is cast during manufacture. Malleable castings, however, may have a part number stamped on them.

2. Spark Test

Sparks from metal when held against a grinder provide a useful guide to identity of ferrous metals. Always wear goggles when doing a spark test.

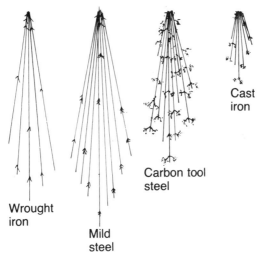

Cast
iron

Carbon tool
steel

Wrought
iron

Mild
steel

Fig. 47. Spark patterns of common ferrous metals

Metal	Spark colour near grinding wheel	Spark colour at end	Volume of sparks
Wrought iron	straw	white	large
Mild steel	white	white	large
Carbon tool steel	white	white	medium
Cast iron	dull red	straw	small

To help learn the colour and type of spark pattern, grind samples of metal of known identity. A cold chisel is made of carbon tool steel; cast iron can be identified visually and mild steel will be found on the new metal storage rack.

3. Filing Test

The first two tests will identify iron and steel. The hardness of the metal can be checked with a file. Mild steel will be easy to cut, medium-carbon steel much harder, and the file will make almost no impression on high-carbon steel.

4. Sawing Test

To help with learning how to identify metals, test samples with a saw. This test will not do when identifying a metal component before making a repair. Test by sawing about one-third of the way through a sample of metal, ideally about 12 mm thick. Make sure the metal is securely held in a vice and then hit the material near the saw cut with a 1 kg (2 lb) hammer.

- Low-carbon steel will bend over some way before breaking.
- Medium-carbon steel will only bend slightly before it breaks.
- Cast iron will snap almost immediately.

NON-FERROUS METALS

There is very little use for non-ferrous metals in the manufacture of farm equipment. Most non-ferrous metals are expensive. When these metals are used, it will be because they have special properties such as high resistance to corrosion or light weight. The more important non-ferrous metals likely to be found on farm machinery and equipment include the following.

Copper

Copper is a very good conductor of both heat and electricity, and has a high resistance to corrosion. It is a soft metal with easy working properties but has the strange property of work hardening. This means that with constant bending or hammering it will become hard and brittle. To return copper to its normal soft condition it is annealed by heating it to a cherry red colour and quenching in clean cold water.

Copper can be joined by soldering or brazing. It cannot be welded. Although very resistant to corrosion, it will eventually corrode and turn green. This green coloured substance, called verdigris, is a layer of copper oxide which forms on exposed surfaces.

The more important uses of copper include water pipes and fittings, electrical components, also some fuel pipes, gaskets and seals for engines. Diesel fuel injector pipes are made of steel. Copper is not strong enough for this purpose.

Brass

An alloy of copper and zinc, brass is a good conductor of heat and electricity, and is resistant to corrosion. Brass can be worked and machined without difficulty. It can be joined by soldering or with an oxy-acetylene welding set, using a brass filler rod. This technique is called brazing.

There are several types of brass, each with varying amounts of copper and zinc. Soft brass may contain up to 40 per cent zinc. It is easy to work and is used to make wire, sheet, strip and tubing.

Hard brass contains more than 40 per cent zinc and is used to make castings. Hard brass is much stronger than soft brass. Its resistance to corrosion makes it a good material to use for components handling liquids—crop sprayer nozzles, water supply fittings, electrical components and bushes are typical examples of its use.

Bronze

An alloy of copper and tin. Small amounts of other metals are added to give special properties to the various types of bronze. Examples include the following.

Gun Metal, contains 88 per cent copper, 10 per cent tin and 2 per cent zinc. It is suitable for making castings, resists corrosion and is a fairly strong metal. Gun metal is used to make bearings.

Phosphor Bronze contains copper, tin and phosphorus. It can be cast and is very resistant to corrosion. It is used to make bushes and bearings.

Babbitt is an alloy of tin, copper and antimony. This is a soft metal with a low melting point. It is used as a bearing material for internal combustion engines. The softer Babbitt metal is bonded on to a steel shell to give the bearing its strength.

Aluminium Bronze. There are a variety of aluminium bronze alloys. A typical example contains about 8 per cent aluminium; it is one of the stronger, corrosion-resistant, copper-based alloys. It has many uses including gear housings and gearbox parts such as selector forks.

Zinc

In its pure form, zinc is a corrosion-resistant metal but tends to be brittle. It is used to coat—galvanise—steel sheets, tanks, pipes, etc. There are several zinc-based alloys. In an almost pure form, it is used to make die castings, a process which allows large numbers of components to be made quickly once the die has been produced.

Tin

Tin is a very expensive metal which is not used in its pure form for agricultural purposes. Its corrosion resistance results in its use as a protective coating for sheet steel, the material known as tin plate. Tin is also an important metal in the production of non-ferrous alloys.

Aluminium

This lightweight metal resists corrosion and is a good conductor of heat and electricity. Pure aluminium is mainly used in sheet form.

An important aluminium alloy is called Duralumin. It has small amounts of copper, manganese and magnesium added to the parent metal. It is easy to work with, light in weight and is stronger than pure aluminium. Duralumin tends to harden with age. Uses include manufacture of tubes, sheets, strip metal, forgings and stampings.

The addition of some copper and zinc produces an alloy suitable for castings. They tend to be brittle and require careful handling. Another aluminium alloy with copper, nickel and magnesium is used to make engine pistons. Aluminium and its alloys will expand more than most metals when heated which means that the heat produced by an engine when it runs will expand an aluminium piston to a greater degree than one made of iron or steel. To allow for this expansion, an aluminium alloy piston will have a slightly smaller diameter than a cast-iron piston made for a cylinder of a certain size.

Lead

A heavy metal with a low melting point, new lead has a bright appearance. A protective layer of dull grey lead oxide soon appears when lead is exposed to the weather. The main use of this metal is in the manufacture of lead acid batteries for tractors and road vehicles. It has many uses in other industries including roof flashings and plumbing but its very high cost has resulted in alternative materials being used where possible.

Solder is an alloy of lead and tin. Like lead, it too has a very low melting point.

OTHER MATERIALS

Plastic

The fact that plastic does not corrode makes it an ideal material for many agricultural applications. Tanks, hoppers and other parts of fertiliser spreaders and crop sprayers are two good examples of non-corrosive plastic taking over from metal.

There are many different types of plastic in use. They can be basically divided into two families:

- *Thermoplastic* materials such as polythene and PVC. This type of plastic will become soft and pliable if subjected to gentle heat. Excessive heat will cause permanent distortion.
- *Thermosetting* plastic changes its shape permanently and cannot be remoulded. Heat will destroy components made of thermosetting plastic.

Thermoplastic Materials

Polythene and *PVC* are two examples of thermoplastic materials used around the farm for items such as waterproof sheeting, guttering and downpipes, tanks, hoppers and buckets.

Alkathene piping is used for cold-water supplies, both inside and outside buildings. *Polypropylene*, a similar material to polythene, is used to make rotproof baler twine.

PTFE resists heat well. It is used to make certain gaskets and seals. Plumbers find PTFE tape useful when making threaded joints to ensure a good seal.

Nylon is used to make small gears and bearings. Its complete resistance to corrosion makes nylon an ideal material for the manufacture of feed mechanisms for grain and fertiliser drills and distributors.

Thermosetting Materials

Bakelite is an important material for electrical insulation. Uses include mains electrical components such as plugs, switches and lamp holders. The distributor cap of a coil ignition system is made of bakelite too.

Polystyrene which is extremely light in weight in its expanded form is an important insulation material for buildings.

Fibre Glass consists of fine strands, or fibres, of glass mixed with plastic resins. Fibre glass is a light, strong, non-corrosive material. It is also an electrical insulator and can be moulded into intricate shapes. Uses of fibre glass include implement guards, safety helmets and bodywork panels for some implements and machines. Although severe vibration may cause fibre glass components to crack, they can be mended with an easy-to-use repair kit.

Rubber

Tyres, drive belts, engine hose pipes, conveyors and root harvester flails are a few examples of the use of rubber in agriculture. Rubber will crack and perish if subjected to strong sunlight for long periods. Oil and grease will also attack it and should be wiped off tyres and other rubber components without delay. Although rubber is an important insulation material for electricity it has been replaced to a great extent by PVC which does not perish.

Timber

Hardwoods, softwoods and manufactured boards such as plywood, chipboard and hardboard have their uses, if somewhat limited, in machinery manufacture. More common uses of timber include trailer sides and floors, bearings for slow-moving shafts, chain tensioners and guides, and also handles for hand and workshop tools. The short life of softwood—unless treated regularly with preservatives—has led to the use of sheet metal and plastics as an alternative to timber.

Other materials used around the farm for special purposes include ceramics and glass. Ceramics, or porcelain, are used for insulators and sprayer nozzles; glass for tractor cabs and bulbs. Canvas is used for conveyors and sheeting.

THINGS TO DO

1. Learn the basic differences between the important types of iron and steel.
2. Carry out the workshop tests on ferrous metals described in this chapter. Make sure you wear goggles when doing the spark test with a grinder.
3. Try to identify the different materials used to make a tractor and a combine harvester.
4. Look for examples of the non-ferrous metals mentioned in this chapter. Most of them can be found in the farm workshop and stores.
5. Find as many different types of plastic as you can around the farm.

QUESTIONS

1. What are the main differences between iron and steel?
2. What is an alloy? Give two examples of both ferrous and non-ferrous alloys.
3. Describe the procedure for hardening and tempering a cold chisel.
4. How is copper annealed?
5. Explain the difference between thermosetting and thermoplastic materials. Give one example, with typical uses, of both types of plastic.

Chapter 5

Soldering and Welding

THESE PROCESSES are used to make a permanent, leak-proof joint between two pieces of metal and require the application of heat. Although soldering and electric welding are described in this chapter there is no substitute for practical instruction for anyone wishing to master these skills. The reader will be well advised to attend one of the many practical welding courses offered by both equipment manufacturers and the local education authorities.

SOLDERING

This is a relatively simple process. The key to success is cleanliness of the surfaces to be joined. Soldering is mainly used for joining steel, copper and brass.

Equipment

A good-quality soldering iron, which may be either electric or flame heated, is the first requirement. An electric iron will cope with most work but for the bigger soldering jobs a flame-heated iron can be an advantage. It also allows soldering to be done away from the workshop where there is no power supply. A small electrician's soldering iron will be very useful for carrying out intricate repairs.

The head of a soldering iron is made of copper. There are various sizes to suit all types of work.

Flux is essential for soldering. It prevents the formation of oxides on the surface of the metal and also helps the solder to flow. Flux is available in liquid or paste form. The most common type is a liquid—killed spirit—sold under a trade name. Flux paste is useful in that it will stay where you put it. Multi-core solder has a resin flux within it which melts with the solder. Most fluxes are corrosive; for this reason all surplus flux should be wiped away after the joint is completed.

Clean surfaces are essential for successful soldering. To achieve this use a clean wire brush and emery cloth.

Solder is an alloy of tin and lead. For example, Tinman's solder contains 50 per cent of each metal. This type of solder is bought in sticks and priced by its weight. For electrical work, use multi-core solder which has its own resin flux in the core. This type of solder is sold on reels or in small containers.

How to Solder

The soldering iron must be at the correct heat, clean and well tinned. The iron is tinned when it has a thin coating of solder on the bit. To tin a soldering iron, clean the bit with a wire brush and then heat it up. Apply some flux then melt a little solder on to the end of the bit.

A satisfactory joint cannot be made if there is any trace of dirt or rust on the metal. When the surfaces are clean, apply some flux and then tin both faces of the joint. Wipe off surplus solder with a clean cloth.

The joint is completed by placing the two tinned faces together and then applying heat with the soldering iron. When the solder runs, hold the two parts firmly together with a clean piece of metal. At the same time remove the soldering iron and allow the solder in the joint to harden. A joint made this way is called a sweated joint.

Mending a leak is one of the more common soldering repairs. Very small holes can be repaired by filling the hole with some solder after a thorough cleaning and the application of some flux. Larger holes will need a patch. Clean an area around the hole and tin the surface. Cut a patch from a thin piece of steel. Clean and tin the patch. For some repairs a piece of a food can which is actually made from tin plate will be suitable. When both surfaces have been tinned, complete the repair by sweat soldering the patch into position.

Fitting olives (see fig. 45) to copper pipe and nipples to Bowden cable are work for the soldering iron. Here again, the parts must be thoroughly clean. Using plenty of flux, tin the parts to be joined. Place the olive in position on the pipe and make a sweated joint with the soldering iron.

Bowden cable nipples have a small hole for the cable which has a recess at one side. Thread the nipple on to the cable after it has been tinned. Spread the end of the cable in the recess and then fill it with solder to secure the nipple in the required position. These small parts will be hot, so handle them with a clean pair of pliers.

Soldering Troubles

Soldering is a skill which will only be gained from practice. The most common error made by the beginner is failing to clean the work properly. When the solder will not stick to a surface, you can be sure that it is not clean enough. Use a file, wire brush or emery cloth to get the surface clean and use plenty of flux.

The soldering iron itself must also be clean and well tinned. Dirt on the iron will be transferred to the joint.

Another basic fault is trying to solder with an iron which is not hot enough. The solder will be difficult to melt and the finished work will be rough.

On the other hand, the iron can also get too hot. A sign of this fault will be a pitted surface finish.

Always use a sufficiently large iron. A small one will never produce enough heat for a big repair but will be ideal for lightweight work such as fixing terminals on to cable.

OXY-ACETYLENE WELDING

Many books have been written on the subject of welding; it is, however, a skill which is best mastered with practical instruction. This section provides the basic information on welding techniques. For more details the reader should refer to one of the excellent operator's handbooks produced by the manufacturers of welding equipment. Armed with this information, the only way to learn how to weld is by plenty of practice at the basic techniques.

Oxy-acetylene welding is a process used to join two pieces of metal by fusing or melting their edges together. This is achieved by directing a flame at the two edges so that a pool of molten metal is formed. It is usual to melt a filler rod into the molten pool to help make the joint.

The flame is produced by burning a mixture of oxygen and acetylene in carefully controlled proportions. This form of welding, which is used on many farms, is more suited to joining thin sections of metal.

By changing the blowpipe, the equipment can be used for cutting metal. A layer of hard surfacing material can also be applied to steel with a gas welding set.

The Equipment

An oxy-acetylene welding set consists of cylinders, regulators, hoses and a blowpipe with a range of nozzles.

The *Cylinders* are colour coded, maroon for acetylene and black for oxygen. To ensure correct assembly, the oxygen cylinder, regulator and hose have right-hand threads. The acetylene fittings have a left-hand thread. The cylinders stand vertically, either on a trolley or secured in a stand. Each cylinder has a shut-off valve, operated by a special key. For most workshops the standard size of cylinder will be required. A much smaller gas welding set, with cylinder capacity of around 0·6 cubic metres (22 cu ft) and a total weight of 32 kg (70 lb) can also be obtained. An outfit of this type can easily be carried to field breakdowns.

The *Regulator* is a screw-operated valve used to control the working pressure of the gas. The thickness of the metal to be welded determines the gas pressure required. The regulator assembly includes two gauges: one registers working pressure and the other indicates cylinder contents.

The *Hoses* connect the blowpipes to the regulators—red for acetylene and blue for oxygen. It is usual to fit a flashback arrester to the regulator and then connect the hose to the arrester outlet. The flashback arrester protects the cylinder if there is a flashback from the blowpipe into the hose. To ensure correct assembly, the acetylene hose connections have a left-hand thread. Hose check valves are fitted at the blowpipe end on the hosepipes. They are non-return valves which prevent oxygen and acetylene mixing in the hoses.

The *Blowpipe* serves as a mixing chamber. It is fitted with one of a range of nozzles to suit thickness of material and type of work. There are two control valves on the blowpipe, controlling the proportions of each gas fed to the flame.

Assembling the Equipment

Stand both cylinders upright and make them secure. Never use a cylinder when it is lying down. Turn on the cylinder valve for a moment to blow any dust or grit from the threads at the top of the cylinder. This is known as snifting the cylinder. Check that the threads are free of any oil or grease.

Screw the regulators into the cylinders, remembering that one has a left-hand thread and the other a right-hand one. Tighten the regulators sufficiently to prevent leaks but do not overtighten them. When assembling a new welding set, blow through the hoses with clean, oil-free air to remove any dust. Fit the flashback arresters and then connect the hoses. Fit check valves to the blowpipe end of the hoses, and then check that they are fitted correctly. Finally, fit the blowpipe. At

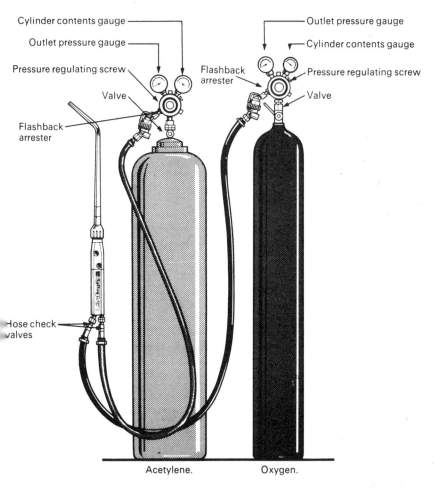

Cylinder contents gauge

Outlet pressure gauge

Pressure regulating screw

Valve

Flashback
arrester

Outlet pressure gauge

Cylinder contents gauge

Pressure regulating screw

Valve

Flashback
arrester

Hose check
valves

Acetylene.   Oxygen.

Fig. 48. Oxy-acetylene welding set

each stage of assembly the equipment should be cleared of dust by allowing the gas to flow for a moment. This is known as purging.

The equipment is now ready for use. Don't use excessive force when closing the blowpipe valves, frequent overtightening will damage them. Always purge a nozzle after it has been fitted to the blowpipe and before attempting to light it.

Protective Clothing

Goggles should be worn at all times. They should have tinted glass to protect the eyes and at the same time give the operator a proper view of the work. The beginner should consult the local welding supplies depot for advice on the correct shade of goggle glass. Details are also given in the Protection of Eyes Regulations.

Leather gloves and a leather apron should be worn when using cutting equipment. Overalls made of nylon are not suitable for welding as any sparks coming into contact with this material will melt it.

Special precautions are needed when working with galvanised steel. Dangerous fumes are given off, so good ventilation is essential and it is a wise precaution to wear a respirator where any amount of this work is done.

Lighting the Blowpipe

First, fit the correct size of nozzle for the work in hand. Table 16 indicates nozzle sizes for various thicknesses of steel for a popular model of blowpipe.

The information in the table is for guidance only, settings will vary according to conditions, material, etc. Gas pressures are shown in bar. 1 bar is equal to 14·7 lbf/in². This makes 0·1 bar equal to 1·47 lbf/in².

When the nozzle has been fitted, place the spindle key on the acetylene (fuel gas) cylinder valve and turn it on slowly. Open the acetylene control valve on the blowpipe, then adjust the working

Table 16. Selection of welding blowpipe nozzles

| Mild steel thickness | | | Nozzle size | Operating pressures | | | |
| | | | | acetylene | | oxygen | |
mm	in	SWG		bar	lbf/in²	bar	lbf/in²
0·9	—	20	1	0·14	2	0·14	2
1·2	—	18	2	0·14	2	0·14	2
2	—	14	3	0·14	2	0·14	2
2·6	—	12	5	0·14	2	0·14	2
3·2	$\frac{1}{8}$	10	7	0·14	2	0·14	2
4	$\frac{5}{32}$	8	10	0·21	3	0·21	3
5	$\frac{3}{16}$	6	13	0·28	4	0·28	4
6·5	$\frac{1}{4}$	3	18	0·28	4	0·28	4
8·2	$\frac{5}{16}$	0	25	0·42	6	0·42	6
10	$\frac{3}{8}$	4/0	35	0·63	9	0·63	9

Note. The units bar and lbf/in² (pounds force per square inch) are used to measure pressure.

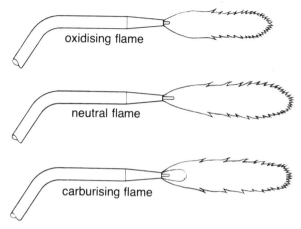

Fig. 49. Welding flames

pressure by turning the pressure regulator screw. Close the blowpipe valve. Repeat the procedure for the oxygen valve.

To light the blowpipe, turn on the acetylene control valve on the blowpipe and ignite the gas. A spark lighter, held at a right angle to the nozzle, is the safest way to light the gas. Adjust the acetylene valve until the flame burns without trace of smoke. The oxygen valve is now opened and adjusted until the required flame is obtained.

- A *Neutral flame* is obtained by opening the oxygen valve until the flame burns with a sharply defined white cone at the tip of the nozzle. A neutral flame is used for most welding work including cast iron and mild steel.
- An *Oxidising flame* is used for welding brass and bronze. It is obtained by closing the acetylene valve slightly until a flame with a shorter cone than the neutral flame appears.
- A *Carburising flame* has an excess of acetylene. It is set by opening the acetylene control valve until a slight feather appears at the end of the cone. A carburising flame is used for hard surfacing, it gives up carbon when used to heat steel.

The beginner should practise setting the three different flames before progressing further.

To extinguish the blowpipe, first close the acetylene control valve and then the oxygen valve. Remember to avoid overtightening the valves. Close the cylinder valves, slacken the regulator screws and then open the blowpipe valves to release any pressure in the hoses. The oxygen valve should be opened first and then the acetylene valve. Check that the pressure gauges register zero.

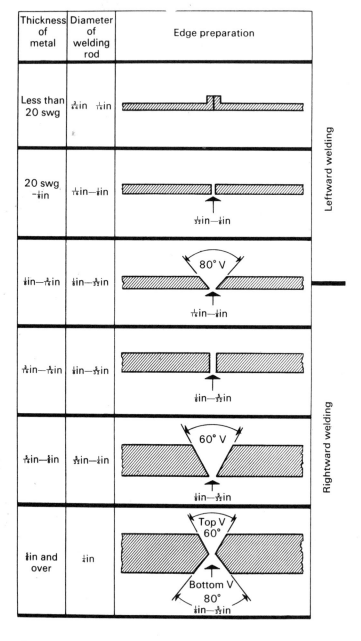

Fig. 50. Edge preparation for butt welding mild steel

There is an exception to this shutting-down procedure. If trouble is experienced with frequent backfire, extinguish the flame by turning the oxygen valve off first.

Edge Preparation

Correct edge preparation is important and fig. 50 shows preparation requirements for various metal thicknesses. It should be noted that a gap is left between the two pieces of metal, except for very thin sections, to allow for expansion of the metal and to ensure good penetration of the filler metal. It is usual to tack—make very small welds—the two plates in position before proceeding with the weld itself.

An oxy-acetylene cutter will make edge preparation of the thicker sections a simple matter and will also save time. Thinner sections should be given a vee edge with a grindstone.

Rods and Fluxes

There are many types of filler rod suitable for a wide range of metals and for hard surfacing. For some techniques, a flux is required. Flux is a chemical powder or paste which cleans the weld metal and prevents oxidation during welding or brazing. You must refer to welding rod charts for details of rods and fluxes. Some common examples of welding rods include copper-coated mild steel rod for welding mild steel, a high-silicon cast-iron rod for welding cast iron and copper-based rods for brazing or bronze welding.

Flux is required for cast-iron welding and for brazing; it should be used in a well-ventilated area.

Rod size is important too; as a general guide the rod should be slightly less in diameter than the thickness of the metal being welded (see fig. 50).

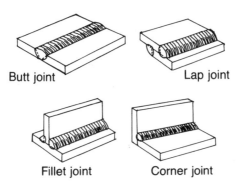

Butt joint   Lap joint

Fillet joint   Corner joint

Fig. 51. Basic welding joints

Welding Techniques

Leftward welding is carried out by pointing the tip of the nozzle forward in the direction of the weld with the filler rod moved along in front of the blowpipe. Work starts at the right and moves to the left. This technique is used for thin-section sheet steel up to about 5 mm ($\frac{3}{16}$ in). It is also the method used for cast iron and ferrous metals. As the blowpipe is moved forwards it is also given a slight sideways motion (weaving) to ensure that both edges melt at the same rate. (Reverse the technique if you are left-handed.)

Rightward welding is the technique for welding steel plate over 5 mm. Some edge preparation is needed (see fig. 50 for details). The weld is started at the left and the blowpipe is moved towards the right with the filler rod following the nozzle. The filler rod is given a circular motion as the blowpipe is moved steadily along the joint. This technique is faster than leftward welding.

Workshops equipped with both gas and electric welding equipment offer a choice of method for joining thicker sections of metal. It is likely that electric welding will be preferred for metals over 5 mm thick.

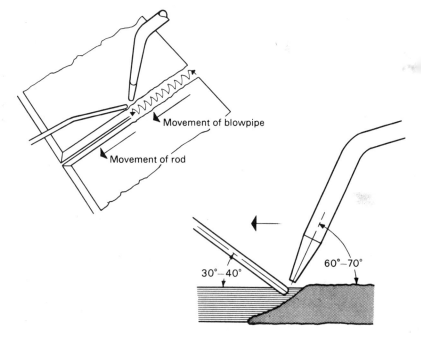

Movement of blowpipe

Movement of rod

30°–40°

60°–70°

Fig. 52. Leftward welding technique

Positional welding is a term used to describe welding in various planes other than on a flat surface. The basic techniques of leftward and rightward welding should be mastered before the beginner ventures on to more difficult work. An example of positional welding is vertical welding which requires the blowpipe to be moved vertically upwards with the filler rod above the nozzle.

Bronze welding is used for joining two pieces of cast iron or copper. This technique is also suitable for joining two dissimilar metals. There are special rods made for a variety of metals and flux is required. Rods

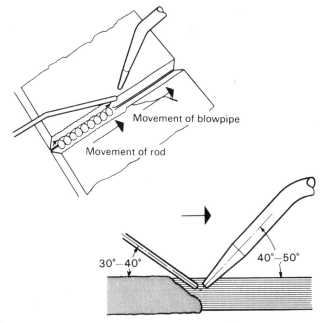

Fig. 53. Rightward welding technique

used include silicon-bronze for copper and brass, and nickel-bronze for brazing steel and malleable iron.

Bronze welding process requires that the edges to be joined should be brought to a dull red heat before the filler metal is applied. Castings will normally require pre-heating before repair. This prevents fracture of the component through uneven heat application and cooling.

Hard surfacing is another technique for the oxy-acetylene welding set. This process involves the depositing of a hard-wearing surface on to steel or cast iron. It is useful for extending the life of soil-wearing parts on cultivation and root harvesting machinery. A carburising

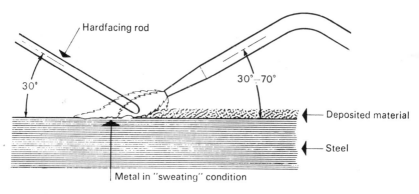

Fig. 54. Hard surfacing technique

flame is used for this technique. The steel is brought to a dull red heat and the hard surfacing filler rod is deposited on this surface. The metal should be allowed to cool slowly. The surface should be free of rust and scale; a flux is normally required.

Maintenance of Welding Nozzles

Nozzles must be treated carefully. Never use the nozzle as a hammer or a lever. The hole in the nozzle should be cleaned with the proper tool. Nozzle reamers, supplied in a handy case, are available from suppliers of welding equipment. It is important to keep the holes in nozzles clear and the end face should be clean and square. Some fine emery cloth placed on a firm, flat surface can be used to clean the end face. After cleaning the face, the hole is cleaned with a reamer of the correct size. Never attempt to enlarge the size of the hole.

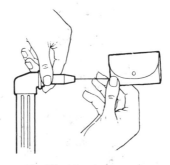

Fig. 55. Nozzle cleaning

OXY-ACETYLENE CUTTING

The principle of an oxy-acetylene cutter is that metal is brought to red heat and then a jet of oxygen is used to blow the molten metal away to form a hole or slot in the metal. Much higher working pressure is required for the oxygen supply. With a little practice the beginner can soon cut through steel cleanly and accurately.

The blowpipe has two control valves, one for oxygen, the other for acetylene. A third control, a lever, is used to release a jet of oxygen through the centre of the nozzle once the metal has been heated.

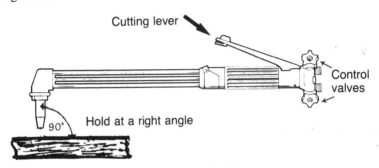

Fig. 56. Oxy-acetylene cutting blowpipe

Lighting the Blowpipe

Set the oxygen and acetylene working pressures to suit nozzle size and thickness of metal. The adjusting screws on the regulators are used. (see table 17 for oxygen and acetylene working pressures for a range of metal thicknesses and nozzle sizes.)

Once the pressures have been set, light the acetylene and adjust the flame until all smoke has cleared. Turn on the oxygen valve and adjust the control until you can see the clear white cone of a neutral flame at the nozzle tip. The nozzle has a ring of small neutral heating flames. The torch is now ready for use. Close the acetylene valve followed by the oxygen valve when extinguishing the flame. The full procedure for shutting off the blowpipe is the same as that for a welding blowpipe.

Cutting Technique

Place the material to be cut in a convenient position, well away from combustible material. Use a cramp or a heavy weight to prevent the work moving while it is being cut. Don't cut close to the floor, especially if it is concrete. Clean off any rust or scale on the surface.

Mark the line of cut, a line drawn with a piece of brass welding rod ground to a point will give a clear mark which doesn't burn off and can be seen clearly through goggles. To help cut a straight line, place a straight metal strip on the workpiece and use it to guide the cutting nozzle. A guide wheel, which also controls the height of the nozzle above the metal can be fitted to a cutting blowpipe to make the work easier, especially for the beginner.

When all is prepared, including the wearing of goggles, light the blowpipe in readiness to start cutting. Place the nozzle at the furthest side of the metal and heat the edge. When the edge is red hot press the cutting lever until it is fully open. This releases a jet of oxygen which blows away the molten steel. Move the cutter across the work at a steady rate. Cutting speed will depend on thickness of material (see table 17). Very thick steel plate, unlikely to be encountered on the farm, will require a large supply of gas.

Table 17. Pressure settings for cutting blowpipes

Plate thickness		Nozzle size	Oxygen		Acetylene		Approx cutting speed	
mm	in		bar	lbf/in²	bar	lbf/in²	mm/min	in/min
6	$\frac{1}{4}$	$\frac{1}{32}$	1·8	25	0·14	2	430	17
13	$\frac{1}{2}$	$\frac{3}{64}$	2·1	30	0·21	3	360	14
25	1	$\frac{1}{16}$	2·8	40	0·14	2	280	11
50	2	$\frac{1}{16}$	3·2	45	0·14	2	200	8

Holes can be cut in metal with a cutting blowpipe. Mark the position of the hole and then heat a section of the steel within the area of the hole. When it is red hot, operate the cutting lever until a hole is pierced. Next cut towards the edge of the required hole at normal cutting speed and then complete the cut.

Good ventilation is essential when cutting galvanised or painted material. Clean the surface as much as possible first. It helps to improve the cut if the nozzle is held at a slight angle so that it tends to undercut the surface coating.

When the cut is complete, remove any slag with a chipping hammer, and if required, the edge can be trimmed on a grinder.

Maintenance of the Nozzle

The cutting nozzle can be cleaned with reamers in the same way as a welding blowpipe. The end of the nozzle should be kept clean and square. Use the correct size of reamer to clean the holes. Under no circumstances should these holes be enlarged.

Safety

- If it is necessary to weld a fuel tank, clean it thoroughly to remove the fumes. It will be safer if the tank is almost filled with water.
- When working with galvanised steel, dangerous fumes are given off. Good ventilation is essential, and it is a wise precaution to wear a face mask.
- Don't cut or weld close to combustible materials. Keep a fire extinguisher near the welder. An asbestos smothering blanket and sand buckets should also be provided. Avoid wearing nylon overalls, as this material is affected by sparks.
- Cylinders should be stood upright. Avoid rolling them as this may damage the valve. Always shut the valves before moving cylinders on a trolley.
- Do not allow oil or grease to get on the cylinders. High-pressure oxygen reacts violently with oil and grease and may explode.
- Check regulators, hoses and blowpipes at frequent intervals; discard any damaged equipment.
- Use a brush to apply soapy water to any joint suspected of leaking. Bubbles will appear if there is a leak. Never check for leaks with a naked flame.
- *Flashback* is the return of flame from the nozzle to the hose and even into the regulator. *Backfire* is the return of flame into the body of the blowpipe; it makes a screeching noise and the flame usually goes out. When the flame is suddenly extinguished, turn off the oxygen valve and then the acetylene valve. Check working and cylinder pressures for correct setting. Allow one gas at a time to flow from the nozzle by opening the control valves, which will purge the hoses and blowpipe. On completion of these checks and precautions, relight the blowpipe.

ELECTRIC-ARC WELDING

Most farm workshops have an electric-arc welder, powered by mains or an engine-driven generator. An electric welder is ready for use as soon as the power is turned on. It lacks the flexibility of the more portable gas-welding equipment but this can be overcome with a rather more expensive generator-driven model.

Electric welding is easier to learn than gas welding, and it is faster too. However, welding thin-section metal, below about 3 mm, takes some practice before a proficient standard can be attained. There is a tendency to use too much heat and, as a result, holes are burnt in the metal.

The oxy-acetylene set makes cutting a simple process but this is not the case with an electric arc welder. Small sections can be cut by using a high amperage—heat—setting. The cut edge will be rather rough. Ordinary mild steel rods can be used, alternatively special-purpose cutting rods can be obtained.

The arc-welding process involves the creation of an electric arc between a welding rod (electrode) and the workpiece (earth). The heat from the arc melts the two edges of the plates to be joined. The molten electrode also serves as a filler rod. The arc creates a gas shield which protects the molten pool of metal from the effects of the atmosphere (oxidation). The electrodes are coated with flux. As the molten metal is deposited, a layer of slag forms over the weld which provides a shield from oxidation while the weld cools. After cooling, the slag is chipped away.

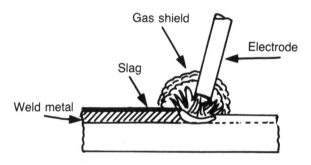

Fig. 57. Formation of an electric arc weld

Welding Equipment

The electric-arc welder is basically a transformer, connected to either single- or three-phase supply. The transformer reduces mains voltage and at the same time increases the amperage (rate of current flow). Most welding sets offer a choice of two voltages, each with a range of amperage settings. A typical welder will have output voltages of 60 or 80 volts. The low-voltage output is used for most general work. The higher-voltage output would be used for welding sheet metal and special electrodes.

Output amperage is selected with a control knob on the welder. Some models have a range of fixed amperage settings, others have a stepless control which gives an infinite range of settings. The stepless control is better as it allows the output to be increased by a few amps if required.

There are two heavy cables from the welder. One is connected to the electrode holder and the other to the earth clamp. The welding equipment must also include a chipping hammer for removing slag, a wire brush and some cramps for holding parts in position while they are welded. Magnetic holders, suitable for holding two pieces of steel in a variety of positions, are a useful welding aid.

Electric welders are either air- or oil-cooled. At one time all transformers had to be oil-cooled but improvements in design have meant that most modern welding sets are air-cooled. Where oil-cooled welders are used (they are desirable where continuous high output is required), it is important to check the oil level at regular intervals. Use the correct grade of oil.

Protective Clothing

Some protective clothing is essential when using an electric welder. A face mask to protect the eyes from glare and the face from the effects of ultra-violet radiation must be used. Both hand-held face masks and welding helmets are available; a helmet leaves both hands free. Welding masks have a dark filter glass, with clear glass covers on each side. The clear glass protects the expensive filter glass from welding spatter—flecks of molten metal and slag. It will be necessary to change the clear glasses from time to time. It is not possible to weld without proper eye protection and even to attempt it would be very foolish. Exposure to ultra-violet light will cause a painful eye condition known as 'arc-eye'. This takes a day or two to disappear but if the condition persists, consult your doctor. Contact lenses should not be worn in the vicinity of an arc welder.

The Protection of Eyes Regulations, 1974, sets out precise requirements for the correct shade of dark filter glasses when electric welding. Filter shades 8/EW or 9/EW should be used when welding with coated electrodes at an output current of up to 100 amps. Shades 10/EW or 11/EW are needed when using coated electrodes at a welding current of 100 to 300 amps. The lower shade number quoted is for welding in bright daylight conditions and the higher number, a darker tint, is needed when welding in darker surroundings such as the farm workshop. You should study the Regulations for the exact requirements or consult your local supplier of welding equipment.

As well as protection from direct glare, precautions are needed to reduce the effect of reflected glare. Place non-reflective, matt green screens around the welding bay or machine under repair. Wall surfaces should have a dark non-reflective finish. Warn people in the vicinity not to look at the glare of a welding set. It can harm the eyes of an onlooker for a distance of up to twelve metres.

Eye protection is also needed when chipping at slag. Clear goggles or a hand mask with clear glass should be used. A leather apron and gauntlet gloves will protect the wearer from heat and weld spatter.

Don't wear rubber boots with trousers tucked inside—this is an open invitation for stray sparks. Wear safety footwear—boots or shoes with steel-reinforced toecaps.

Keep the area around the welding bench tidy and clear of combustible material. Near the welder keep a fire extinguisher which is suitable for dealing with electrical fires (see page 23).

Electrodes

There are many types and sizes of electrodes or welding rods. Information about their amperage setting and advice on their use will be found on the packet. Metals other than iron and steel can also be electric welded. There are special rods to suit these metals. Depositing a layer of hard-surfacing material, again with special rods, is another job for the arc-welding set.

Table 18. Example of amperage settings and use for a typical electrode suitable for general-purpose welding of steel

Thickness of material		Electrode diameter		Typical welding current
mm	SWG/in	mm	SWG	amps
sheet				
0·9–0·7	20–22 SWG	1·5	16	25–50
1·6–0·9	16–20 SWG	2	14	40–65
4–1·6	8–16 SWG	2·5	12	60–95
strip				
up to 6	up to $\frac{1}{4}$ in	3·25	10	90–140
up to 12	up to $\frac{1}{2}$ in	4	8	140–190
over 12	over $\frac{1}{2}$ in	5	6	190–230

Damp electrodes are difficult to use and give poor results, for this reason, it is important to keep welding rods dry. They can be dried but it is much better to store them in a damp-free atmosphere. A simple storage cabinet can be made by fitting a low-power electric light bulb, left on all the time, in a suitable cupboard. Heat from the bulb will maintain a dry atmosphere.

Manufacturers' leaflets provide much information about welding rods and their use. Settings will differ according to type of material, size of electrode and type of work. The beginner will do well to start off by trying to master the skill of electric welding mild steel. Table 18 provides some guidance on rod size and amperage settings for this. There are a number of suitable rods for mild steel, so where possible refer to the maker's instructions. Where none are available the settings in Table 18 provide a guide.

Using the Welder: Striking an Arc

The first task for the beginner is to learn how to strike an arc. Place a mild steel electrode in the holder and set the amperage according to the thickness of material and rod size. This information will be on the packet. A good earth is essential. The metal to be used for practice should be clean, rust free and at least 6 mm thick. Place the metal on the welding bench and attach the welder earth clamp to the bench. If the bench is not made of steel, the earth clamp must be fixed to the workpiece.

Take a comfortable stance, with your legs slightly apart and your body held in a steady position. It may be easier if you support your body against the bench or even sit on a stool of suitable height. The weight of the electrode cable can be partly taken off the hand by passing it over one shoulder. Once you are comfortable, hold the mask in front of your

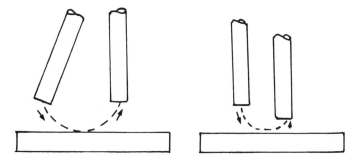

Fig. 58. Striking an arc

face, turn on the welder and prepare to strike your first arc. To do this, hold the tip of the electrode about 25 mm from the metal surface and move it sideways and downwards, rather like striking a match. This should cause a bright flash which indicates some success. Once the arc is started, it must be kept going. Move the electrode upwards slightly and try to maintain a small gap between the metal and the end of the rod. As soon as the arc is going well, move the electrode across your body slowly from left to right (if you are right handed).

An arc can also be struck by tapping the electrode on the metal until it flashes and then proceeding as described above. The beginner will have problems with maintaining the correct arc length and will find that the electrode sticks to the metal, usually with an alarming hum coming from the welding transformer. The arc length is the distance from the tip of the electrode to the metal being welded.

To free an electrode which has stuck to the workpiece, give the holder a sharp twist. If it does not come away immediately, turn off the power and try again. You must keep the face mask in position while freeing a stuck electrode. It is likely that the flux coating on the electrode will be broken away round the tip during the freeing of the rod. In this condition, it may be difficult to strike an arc. The end can be trimmed by drawing it across a piece of scrap metal until the electrode is burnt back to shape.

Some electrodes, known as touch electrodes, will strike when drawn across the metal surface. They are rather more expensive than ordinary electrodes.

Arc Length

Once the arc is struck the electrode will melt, so downward movement is needed to maintain the correct arc length. You cannot measure the arc length but try to keep the tip of the electrode at a distance equal to its

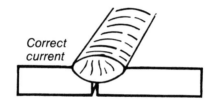

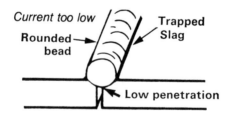

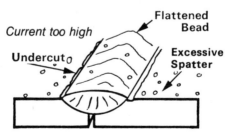

Fig. 59. Effects of incorrect current settings

diameter from the work. The electrode must be moved along at a rate which prevents a large pool of molten metal forming and on thin metals burning a hole.

A loud blowing noise will come from the electrode if the arc is too long. The rod will stick if the arc length is too short.

Once striking and maintaining an arc has been mastered, the next task is to practise making straight runs of weld. Correct speed and current are important. A welding speed which is too slow will produce a wide, high and often lumpy weld deposit. A thin, irregular weld will result if welding speed is too high.

Low current settings cause a lumpy surface finish; slag may be trapped in the weld and penetration of the molten metal into the joint will be poor. It may also be difficult to keep the arc going. When the welding current is too high, the weld bead will be flat; there will be excessive deposits of spatter and, with thin metal, there is every chance that a hole will be burnt in the workpiece.

Weaving is a technique used to make a wide bead of weld. The tip of the electrode is moved sideways in a weaving motion at the same time as it is moved forward. The amount of sideways movement will depend on metal thickness, electrode size and current setting.

Welding Techniques

Space permits only outline detail of the various welding techniques. There are many excellent textbooks and instruction manuals available to anyone wishing to study the subject in depth. Armed with such information, there is still no substitute to workshop instruction followed by plenty of practice.

The basic joints for electric welding, butt and fillet, are similar to those for gas welding. These joints are illustrated in fig. 51.

The work must be clean with all traces of rust, scale and grease removed. Select the correct size electrode and set the amperage to suit. It is important to avoid distortion during welding. A small tack weld at each end of the joint, more if the joint is a long one, will hold the material in position.

Butt Joints

Using the downhand technique—working on the flat—a butt joint is made by placing the two plates close together but not touching. A small gap is left to allow for expansion of the metal. It also ensures good penetration of the filler rod metal into the joint. Rod size, amperage setting and gap will depend on material size. The following table gives a guide; experience will enable you to vary these settings according to conditions.

Table 19. Basic settings for butt welding mild steel

Metal thickness mm	Electrode size mm	Electrode size SWG	Amperage settings	Notes
up to 2·5	2·0	14	60	no gap required
2·5–3·0	2·5	12	90	1·5 mm gap
3·0–6·0	3·25	10	120	3 mm gap
6·0–10·0	4·0	8	170	5 mm gap
10·0–12·0	5·0	6	200	vee both edges to 45°. Leave 3 mm of vertical surface at bottom of plates. Plate gap to be 3 mm

Place the two plates on the welding bench, set welder to required current output and check that the earth clamp is secure. Make a small tack weld near the ends of the joint and then weld the two edges together.

Thicker sections may require more than one run. Always chip off the slag before adding a further run of weld.

Fillet Welding

This joint may have a weld on either one or both sides of the vertical plate. The weld can be made in two ways. The base plate can be placed on a flat surface and the vertical plate held in position ready for welding (see fig. 60a). An alternative method allows the easier downhand welding technique to be used. After tacking the plates in position, the work is supported on the bench so that the weld can be made horizontally.

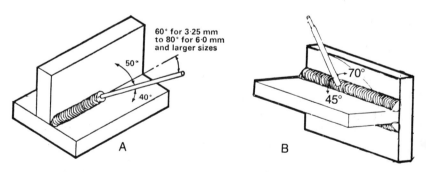

Fig. 60. Fillet welding

Large fillet welds will need more than one run. Chip away all slag between each run of weld. It is also important to chip slag from tack welds.

The fillet weld made in the horizontal–vertical position (fig. 60a) requires care to ensure that there is no undercutting of the vertical plate. Undercutting will be avoided if the electrode angle shown in the diagram is maintained and the arc is kept short.

Positional Welding

A term which includes welding in the overhead and vertical positions. Special electrodes needed for this work have a flux coating which helps to hold the weld metal in position while it cools. Correct electrode angles are important (see fig. 61).

Overhead and vertical–downward welding need a short arc and a fairly high amperage setting to force the molten filler metal into the joint.

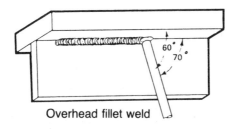

Overhead fillet weld

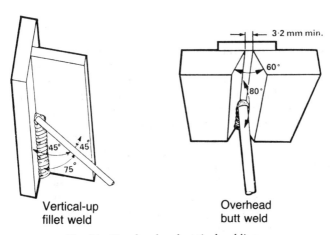

Vertical-up
fillet weld

Overhead
butt weld

Fig. 61. Overhead and vertical welding

Vertical–upward welding also needs a short arc but a lower amperage setting. The electrode should bisect the angle for a vertical fillet. The vertical–upward technique keeps the weld surface sloping down and the slag runs clear without becoming trapped in the weld metal.

These positional welding techniques will take the beginner, or occasional welder, much practice to master. Except on a machine which cannot be tipped upside down for repairs it is usually possible to place the parts to be welded in a position which allows the somewhat easier downhand welding technique to be used.

Hard Surfacing

Many earth-wearing parts can usefully be hard surfaced with special electrodes applied with an electric welder. You can extend the life of new shares, tines, etc., by hard surfacing them before they are first used; similarly, used parts can be rebuilt and then hard surfaced to reduce replacement costs.

New material requires no preparation, other than removal of rust and scale, before it is hard surfaced. Worn surfaces and edges will need a trim with a grinder.

There are several types of hard-surfacing rod. They are normally applied in beads, alongside one another, or in a chequer plate pattern over a large surface area. More than one layer may be applied if required. Most hard-surface electrodes are used with the high-voltage setting on the welding plant; amperage settings will depend on electrode size. Look for these settings on the electrode packet.

Welding Cast Iron

Repairing white cast iron (chilled) and some types of malleable iron often results in fresh cracks appearing after the weld is complete. Other forms of cast iron, particularly grey iron castings can usually be welded with complete success. There is always a risk of fresh cracks appearing during the cooling period but this is a chance well worth taking. Cast-iron welding will be more effective if the mechanic has become proficient with the basic welding techniques.

Cast iron contracts rather quickly when it cools. This sets up internal stresses in the metal which may cause a fresh crack or fracture. Rapid cooling has a hardening effect on the metal and makes it rather brittle. Mild steel electrodes produce a brittle joint because they take up carbon from the parent cast iron; so cast iron repaired with mild steel rods must be cooled very slowly to reduce these risks. It is far better to use a nickel-based, cast-iron electrode which does not have this effect on the parent metal.

The damaged part can be pre-heated before it is welded. This should prevent cracks appearing after the job is complete. Another remedy is to peen (hammer lightly) the surface of weld metal immediately it is deposited. Measures can also be taken to slow the rate of cooling after the weld is completed.

The application of pre-heating in the farm workshop will only go as far as applying heat in the area of the fracture with an oxy-acetylene blowpipe. Industrial processes include pre-heating in ovens which have precise temperature control. Cooling in the workshop can be controlled by covering the casting with an asbestos blanket or dry sand. Again, in industry, cooling can be controlled in ovens if such precautions are necessary. Any broken casting which is costly or impossible to replace can be taken to a specialist if the mechanic feels the job is beyond his ability or requires special equipment.

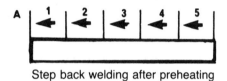

Step back welding after preheating

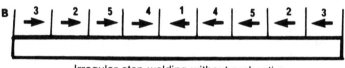

Irregular step welding without preheating

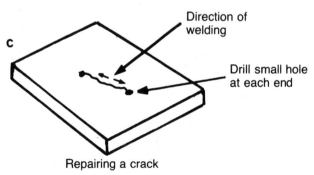

Repairing a crack

Fig. 62. Hints on welding cast iron

The part to be welded should be clean and free from grease. Preparation depends on thickness of the material and the degree of accuracy required. Edges of a fracture can be ground to a vee, provided there is sufficient thickness of metal. To ensure an accurate repair, the original line of fracture should be left intact. This allows a perfect match of the two parts.

Tack weld the parts and check for correct positioning. If the casting has been pre-heated, use a large electrode and make short beads of weld in a step-back procedure. This will further reduce the risk of fresh cracks. A casting which has not been pre-heated should be repaired with a small electrode allowing a lower heat setting. Deposit short beads of weld (not more than 50 mm long) in a planned system to prevent overheating in one area of the casting.

Nickel-based electrodes give a bead of machinable weld which, after cooling, can be trimmed with a grinder. It can also be used to build up broken parts, which on completion of the welding process can be filed to the required shape.

Cracks in castings can also be repaired with the electric welder. A small hole should be drilled at each end of the crack (see fig. 62c), and then repaired with a bead of weld applied from the centre outwards.

Electrodes for Cutting

It is possible to buy special electrodes for cutting away metal, weld deposits, bolt heads, etc. They require a very high amperage setting. This type of rod can also be used to prepare for a weld by gouging out a groove in a crack or trimming off the edges of two plates.

Carbon Arc Equipment

An attachment connected to the basic welding set allows the electric arc welder to be used for heating and brazing. It produces a flame by electrical means which is suitable for brazing thin sections of metal, flame cleaning and heating metal for bending to shape or straightening damaged parts. The equipment consists of a carbon torch unit and special carbon rods which give the flame. A low amperage setting is used for brazing; heating techniques must have a high setting.

Welding Problems

Follow the basic rules of electric welding and there will be very few problems when welding the common ferrous metals. Welding techniques for special steels and non-ferrous metals require special treatment—the reader should study a welding manual before attempting this work.

Table 20. Electric welding faults

Fault	Likely causes
Difficulty in striking an arc	Low amperage setting Poor earth connection Dirty metal Damp or damaged electrode
Poor penetration of weld metal	Amperage setting too low Insufficient gap Electrode too large Electrode at incorrect angle
Slag trapped in weld metal	Not chipped away between welds Gap too narrow Welding arc not continuous, allowing slag to be trapped during weld Rust or scale left on metal
Joint not fused together correctly	Amperage setting too low Electrode too small (on heavier plate) Incorrect electrode angle Electrode speed too high Rust and scale on edges of joint
Undercutting edges of joint (weakens joint and traps slag)	Amperage too high Arc too long Electrode too large Incorrect electrode angle Weaving speed too fast at each end of movement on wide joints; straight runs avoid this

The following points will solve most problems with downhand welding. Only practice will eliminate faults with positional welding techniques.

- Keep electrodes dry.
- Keep the welder and terminals clean.
- Choose the proper electrode for the job and select the correct amperage. Check the packet for details.

- Hold the electrode at the correct angle.
- Maintain a short arc. A long arc on thin metal will burn holes.
- Always chip away slag before making a repeat weld.
- For downhand welding, use the lowest possible amperage setting. When the setting is too high, it will burn the metal and produce a weak joint. A setting which is too low gives a poor weld and it will be difficult to maintain the arc.
- Maintain a good earth connection and don't try to weld dirty or corroded metal. It will be difficult to strike an arc in these circumstances.
- Correct gap and tack welds will overcome most problems with distortion.
- Good welding is only possible when the operator is in a comfortable position, using the correct arc length at the right speed.
- Never weld without correct eye protection and consider others in the vicinity before striking an arc.

THINGS TO DO

1. Practise soldering with some odd pieces of metal. Do remember that clean surfaces are essential.
2. Obtain a copy of a welding operator's manual if you wish to find out more about welding techniques, especially for non-ferrous metals.
3. Learn how to set the three basic welding flames used for oxy-acetylene welding.
4. Always wear suitable eye protection when using a welder.
5. Study the information given on some welding rod packets and compare the suggested settings for different types of electrode.

QUESTIONS

1. Why is flux used when making a soldered joint?
2. Which technique should be used for gas welding mild steel with a thickness of 6 mm?
3. What is snifting? How and why is it done?
4. How should electric welding electrodes be stored?
5. Give three reasons for poor penetration of weld metal when making a joint.

Chapter 6

Dealing with Corrosion

ALL METALS corrode. The layer of corrosion on some of them, such as lead, provides a protective coating which stops further decay. However, most types of iron and steel will rust at a rapid rate if they are not protected from the effects of the weather and farm chemicals. Rust weakens metal and reduces the efficiency and working life of implement parts such as plough mouldboards and shares. Rust will also seize parts which should move to allow adjustment. In both cases time and money will be wasted—it is far quicker and less expensive to prevent corrosion than to repair the damage at a later date.

There are several preventative measures available to the farmer in the fight against corrosion. Some last for a short period, others are long term or permanent. Storage of machinery and equipment under cover is the first step. Buildings are expensive but so are the repair bills which will result from corrosion if the protection of the more valuable machines is neglected. The use of non-corrosive materials, such as plastic and stainless steel, overcomes some problems, particularly with crop sprayers and fertiliser distributors.

All machinery should be cleaned thoroughly after work is completed. Leaving this chore for a rainy day may be too late. It takes very little time for damp chemicals to cause serious rusting and even seizure of parts which are in direct contact with the chemical. In recent years the pressure washer has become a popular tool on farms. It does an excellent job but care must be taken to prevent water entering places where even more corrosion will occur. It is not a good idea to wash the inside of a combine harvester. An industrial vacuum cleaner or the use of compressed air will prove a better method, once the bulk of the dirt has been removed by hand. Take care when washing engines; water should not be allowed near electrical equipment, engine breathers, etc. After pressure washing, it is important to check that the machine is dry before it is put away. Parts with no paint left on them should be given a coat of paint or rust preventative.

CLEANING EQUIPMENT: WIRE BRUSHES

Dirt, mud and chemicals can be removed with a pressure washer, steam cleaner or a hose pipe. Rust and other hard deposits require some form of abrasive cleaning such as wire brushing or sand blasting.

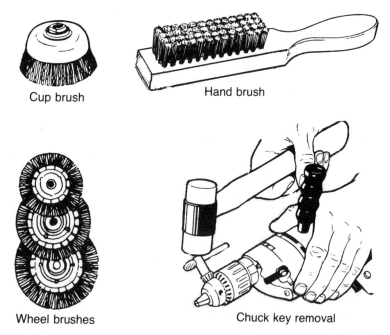

Cup brush   Hand brush

Wheel brushes   Chuck key removal

Fig. 63. Wire brushes

Hand wire brushes, or scratch brushes, will be found in every workshop to cope with all the small cleaning jobs. A wire brush fitted in an electric drill will make the cleaning of large areas less tedious. It should be noted that there is a tendency for high-speed wire brushes to polish the surface of the metal.

The more common types of wire brush used in electric drills are the wheel brush, a small version of the wire brush used on a bench grinder (see fig. 28), and the cup brush. Other shapes and size of wire brush suitable for cleaning small holes and awkward corners can be obtained. Always make sure that the wire brush is secure in the drill chuck before it is used. Some wire brushes have a threaded shank which is screwed into the drill spindle after removing the chuck. To remove the chuck, first place the chuck key in position. Hold the drill so that the key is slightly above horizontal and on the right-hand side of the drill. Strike the chuck key with a downward blow, using a light hammer. This should loosen the chuck after which it can be unscrewed by hand.

Hold the drill at an angle to the work and do not use excessive pressure. It is a wise precaution to wear clear goggles or protective glasses. The drill can be fitted to a bench stand, leaving the hands free for cleaning small parts such as engine valves, bolts, etc.

ABRASIVE SHEETS

There are many kinds of abrasive sheet suitable for various materials and trades. Different grades are available for each type and these can lead to some confusion. Table 21 gives some guidance on the subject.

Emery Cloth

This, the most common type of abrasive material, is sold in sheets, discs and rolls. Emery *cloth* is a cloth-backed abrasive which can be used in thin strips if required; Emery *paper* does not have the strength of the cloth. There are various grades from coarse to extra fine.

Wet-and-Dry Paper

This paper uses silicon carbide as the abrasive material. It is similar to emery but can be used wet or dry. When used wet, it is dipped in water which acts as a lubricant and prevents clogging. Wet-and-dry paper is used to prepare for a high-grade surface finish.

Silicon carbide is also used to make fibre-backed abrasive discs for electric drills. Sold in various diameters and grades, silicon carbide discs are suitable for cleaning and sanding metal.

Aluminium Oxide Paper

An abrasive paper sold in disc and sheet form. The handyman's aluminium oxide disc is paper backed but a much tougher and more expensive fibre-backed disc is also available. The abrasive grit, aluminium oxide, is very hard. Grade of abrasive is classified by grit number. An aluminium oxide cloth-backed abrasive is also made.

Tungsten Carbide Discs

A very hard abrasive material fixed to a permanent backing. Available in fine, medium and coarse grits.

Glasspaper

The carpenter's abrasive material: it is frequently, and incorrectly, called sandpaper. Sold in sheet, strip and disc form, glasspaper is made in a range of abrasive grades but is only suitable for rubbing down timber and other soft materials; it is not suitable for metalwork. Another abrasive for wood is garnet paper which is red, has a harder grit and lasts longer than glasspaper.

Cutting Discs

Aluminium oxide and silicon carbide are also used to make cutting discs for portable grinders (see page 68). The construction of the discs is such that it would be dangerous to use sanding discs for cutting or cutting discs for sanding. Aluminium oxide discs are recommended for cutting ferrous metals and silicon carbide discs should be used for cutting non-ferrous metals, masonry, etc.

Table 21. Grades of abrasive paper and cloth

	Emery cloth Grade	Aluminium oxide and silicon carbide Grit	Tungsten carbide Grade	Glasspaper Grade
Very Fine	0	400 320 280 240 220	—	—
Fine	F	180 150 120	Fine	00 (flour) 0 1
Medium	1½ 2 i	100 80 60	Medium	1½ F2 M2
Coarse	2½ 3	50 40 36	Coarse	S2 2½ 3
Very Coarse	3½ 4 4½	30 24 20 16 12	—	—

Using Abrasive Paper

Hand-held sheets should be wrapped round a cork, or wooden, block where a flat surface is required. It is more economical to tear or cut the sheet into smaller parts. Sanding discs must be used on a rubber backing pad screwed into the drill spindle after removing the chuck. Always hold the drill so that one side of the disc is in contact with the metal; it must not be held flat against the surface. Don't apply heavy pressure and keep the disc on the move over the surface with steady sweeping strokes. New discs should be fitted to the pad with a clamping washer and screw. Make sure that the screw is tight and that the washer is properly seated in the centre of the disc backing pad. Goggles should be worn when using abrasive discs with an electric drill.

CLEANERS AND WASHERS

Pressure Washers

Pressure washers have many uses on the farm and in the workshop; both cold-water and hot-water washers are available. The principle of a pressure washer is that a pump forces water through a nozzle at high pressure. The pump may be driven by an electric motor, a stationary petrol or diesel engine, or mounted on a tractor and driven by the power take-off shaft. Hot-water washers have an automatically controlled boiler unit so that the water leaves the nozzle at the required temperature. A typical hot-water pressure washer has a water temperature range of 60° to 130°C. It is possible to introduce detergents and disinfectants automatically into the water if required. A wet sand blasting attachment can also be used with some pressure washers.

Pressure washers have numerous uses in livestock buildings. With the addition of detergent or disinfectant to the water they are used for cleaning out pig pens, calf pens, etc. Machines need washing before storage and in preparation for overhaul. Washing equipment to remove mud, fertilisers and spray chemicals, degreasing tractors and machinery before carrying out repairs and washing down areas of concrete are just a few of the jobs for a pressure washer.

Maintenance

Pressure cleaners require little maintenance. Check belt tension and oil level, where applicable, and protect the machine from damage by frost during the winter.

The power unit should be serviced at regular intervals and you should make sure that all guards are kept in place.

Steam Cleaners

The steam cleaner has been replaced to a great extent by the pressure washer. The principle of the steam cleaner is that a boiler operating on paraffin or light fuel oil heats a supply of water to produce a jet of steam and hot water from a hand lance. An electric motor drives a pump which supplies a steady flow of water to the boiler. The hand lance has a steam jet and is connected to the cleaner by a length of high-pressure steam hose. The spray pattern is changed by fitting different jets.

Typical uses of a steam cleaner include cleaning livestock buildings, degreasing engines and vehicles and washing down farm equipment. Using the cleaner involves working with very hot water and steam so some protective clothing is essential. Rubber boots and waterproof clothing should be worn. Cleaning efficiency will be improved when cleaning greasy equipment if a detergent is used. It is important to use the right detergent: some are abrasive and will damage the water pump, others are not suitable for use with steam and very hot water.

Flame Cleaning

This is a simple method for preparing metal surfaces for repainting. The flame cleaner will give a clean, moisture-free surface which, after a light wire brushing, will be ready for a coat of priming paint.

Flame-cleaning nozzles can be used with an oxy-acetylene welding set. Various widths of flame-cleaning nozzle can be fitted to the basic blowpipe unit giving, for example, a flame width of 50 mm, 100 mm or 150 mm.

Full precautions must be taken to prevent personal injury. Don't flame clean a component or machine if there is even the slightest risk of starting a fire.

Flame-cleaning equipment is also available for use with propane gas, and it is possible to clean very small areas with a small, hand-held butane gas torch.

RUST PREVENTION

Rust can be prevented for short periods by coating bare metal surfaces with oil or grease. This is quite effective if the machine is protected from the weather but sun and rain will soon remove it.

Application of rust preventative solutions will give protection for some months. A coat of paint on a well-prepared surface will give lasting protection but where the surface has been badly corroded there is a risk that rust will break through the surface again.

The use of galvanised or plastic-coated metal will provide almost permanent protection from corrosion. These materials are often used in building construction. Non-corrosive materials such as plastic are used more and more, especially for machinery used to handle farm chemicals. Plastic water pipe is another example of beating corrosion with a substitute material.

Rust Preventative Solutions

The major oil companies offer a range of rust preventative liquids which are ideal for the protection of bright surfaces on ploughs, balers and combines. The protective fluid is mixed with a solvent which evaporates on application, leaving a protective film on the surface of the metal.

De-watering fluids serve two purposes: they displace any water left on the metal surface, and they then deposit a thin protective film which prevents corrosion. The thickness of the film depends on the type of fluid used. Some de-watering fluids leave a thin, soft film which lasts for just a few days. Others will coat a metal surface with a thicker film of either a soft or a medium consistency giving outdoor protection for up to twelve months.

Another type of rust preventative fluid has no de-watering properties. When applied to a dry surface it leaves a thick protective film which lasts for about a year and even longer if the machine is stored under cover. Rust preventative solutions are best applied with a brush.

PAINTING

The quality of a finished paint job will depend on the care taken during the preparation of the surface and the selection of the right type of paint.

Wash the surface with white spirit or other suitable solvent to remove all traces of dirt, oil and grease. White spirit is usually sold as turpentine substitute and is a suitable thinner for most types of paint. Remove any loose or defective paint with a scraper, wire brush or emery cloth. Sometimes it will be necessary to clean off the old paint completely, using either a paint stripper (remover) or a flame gun. Choice of method depends on type of material and the position of the faulty paint in relation to other parts. Don't take risks with flame cleaning if there is any likelihood of starting a fire or damaging other parts of a machine.

Paint strippers are liquid, some water soluble, others solvent based. Take care when using a stripper: it will cause an unpleasant burn if it gets on to your skin. Wash off any splashes without delay. Allow time for the stripper to work before scraping off the old paint. Once the surface is clean, wash it with water or white spirit, depending on type of stripper used. Allow the metal surface to dry and then rub it down with emery cloth or a wire brush.

Types of Paint

Oil-based household paints are not really suitable for repainting farm implements; a quick-drying synthetic enamel is much better. It is possible to buy synthetic enamel in a range of colours to suit those used by most tractor and machinery manufacturers. It can be applied with a brush or a spray gun and gives a tough, high-gloss surface which will resist corrosion and the effects of fuel and lubricants. Most machinery dealers sell synthetic enamel.

Cellulose paint gives the high-quality finish used for road vehicles and similar applications. Cellulose paint, which is normally sprayed after mixing with a special thinner, will have little or no use in the farm workshop.

Priming Paints

A good top coat depends on selection of suitable primer and undercoat paints. Paint consists of a pigment, which gives the colour, a binder to produce the paint film, a solvent which helps the paint flow while it is applied and a drying agent. There are several different types of solvent. For this reason, it is important to use undercoat and primer paints which are compatible (agree) with the gloss finish. The solvents used in the same type of paint may vary from one manufacturer to another, so for best results use undercoat and gloss of the same brand. When the solvents in two paints are not compatible, the surface finish will be poor and wrinkles may appear.

Primer paint is applied first, usually on bare surfaces or where most of the previous paint has worn or corroded away. The common primer paint for timber is pink. It is not suitable for metal. Where serious rusting has occurred, a commonly used primer is red oxide. Two thin coats, mixed with white spirit to dilute the paint slightly, are better than one thick coat. Allow at least an hour between the first and second coat of red oxide zinc chromate primer. The surface must be clean, dust-free and washed with white spirit to remove any traces of oil or grease.

Other priming paints include an aluminium metal primer, a lead-based primer and a glossy primer, usually red or grey, which gives fairly long-term protection without any further treatment. Any paint containing lead must not be used for livestock buildings and equipment if there is any chance of the animals getting to the painted surface. A coat of aluminium primer over red oxide will improve the covering power of the following undercoat.

Rusted surfaces which are pitted may need more drastic treatment. There are a number of preparations on the market which will 'kill' rust. After a thorough wire brushing, the surface is coated with the rust killer. Once dry, a coat of red oxide or other primer can be applied.

Another type of primer paint is a cold galvanising preparation which contains a high proportion of zinc and can be applied with brush or spray gun. It is dry in about one hour after application. This is a rather expensive material but it gives a high resistance to corrosion.

Galvanised iron and steel should not require painting. Sometimes, for decorative reasons, this type of work is done. Weathered galvanised metal will take a paint better than new material. Clean the surface to remove all traces of dust and grease. New material will require a coat of special primer paint: calcium plumbate metal primer containing some lead is the usual recommendation for this work. This treatment is followed by a coat of chromate metal primer and then the undercoat. Weathered galvanised iron and steel should be cleaned down and primed with a chromate metal primer, then undercoated. The primer paints for this work may only be obtainable from specialist paint shops.

Brush Application

A good-quality paint brush is essential. As a new brush will shed some of its bristles, it is a good idea to break it in with undercoating work. After use, clean the brush thoroughly and store it dry. Work the brush on a spare piece of wood to remove as much paint as possible and then wash in white spirit. When the brush is really clean, dry it with some rag and store flat in a box or stand it in a jar with the bristles upwards. For long-term storage, work grease into the bristles and wrap the brush in newspaper. For short periods, put the brush in water or white spirit. The bristles will keep their shape better if the brush is suspended in a jar by passing a long nail through a hole drilled in the handle.

When brush painting, one coat of primer, thinned if necessary with white spirit, will in most cases be sufficient. Allow the primer to dry for at least four hours before applying the undercoat. Allow the undercoat to dry thoroughly. The surface should be lightly rubbed down to provide a key for the top coat. Where a second top coat is required, synthetic enamels should be applied within a few hours. If this is not possible, allow the first top coat to harden, give it a light rub down and after dusting the surface it will be ready for the final coat.

Always read the instructions on the sales leaflet or tin. The information given above is a general guide and should be supplemented with the maker's own instructions.

Replace the lid on the tin as soon as work is finished, making sure it is an airtight fit. When a skin forms on the paint there will still be some small pieces of hard paint left, even after the skin is removed. These pieces will spoil the surface finish. One way to keep air out of a stored paint tin is to put the lid on tight and stand the tin upside down on a shelf. If the tin is stored for some while it must be given a thorough shaking to mix the paint before the lid is taken off. An alternative method is to tip the tin upside down for a few seconds after securing the lid. This should leave a film of paint around the inside of the lid which seals it from the air.

Use a big enough paint brush for the job in hand. Stroke the paint on to the surface, don't dab away with the end of the brush. Paint the awkward and difficult-to-get-at parts first; this should ensure that you do not smother your hands with paint.

Spray Painting

Spraying paint is not as easy as it seems. The novice will find it difficult to control the flow of paint and runs will appear. Good surface preparation is important. Paint for spraying must be thinned, the usual mix being one part of thinners to one part of paint. It is a good idea to mix sufficient paint for the whole job before starting work with the spray gun.

The best results will be obtained with the spray nozzle held between 300 and 450 mm (12 and 18 in) from the surface being painted. Don't move the spray gun through an arc as this will cause an uneven film of paint. Try to keep the nozzle at a right angle to and an even distance from the area being painted.

It is better to put on two thin coats rather than one thick one. Don't let the first coat get too dry before spraying the second coat.

Newspaper, held in place with masking tape can be used to protect parts which do not require spraying. Very small parts can be covered with a thin film of grease.

Successful spray painting requires an operating pressure of 4·0 to 5·5 bar (60–80 psi). A compressor which does not have an air receiver tank is not really suitable for spray painting because the surges of air will given an uneven film of paint. When a compressor without an air tank is used, the spray gun should be operated in short bursts to obtain a relatively even coat of paint.

Water will collect in air receiver tanks, hoses and fittings. It is most important to drain this water from the system before attempting to use a spray gun. Never spray in an area where there is poor ventilation. Always wear a mask. Dust will spoil the surface finish and precautions should be taken to overcome this problem. The area should be kept clean but don't sweep the floor just before you start spraying as dust will remain in the air for some time. The floor area can be dampened with a fine spray of water to keep the dust down for a while. Take care not to get any water on the surfaces which are to be painted.

Select the best spray gun you can afford. Choose one which has an adjustable nozzle that can be set to give a variety of spray patterns and can apply paint to large and small areas with minimum waste of material. After use, clean the spray gun with thinners, making sure that all traces of paint are removed from the nozzle and body of the gun.

Aerosol sprays are handy for touching up paint on vehicles or spraying very small areas but are hardly suitable for general workshop use.

WOOD PRESERVATIVES

Creosote is the usual preservative for farm woodwork. Once a coat of creosote has been applied, it is almost impossible to cover it with paint. Creosote can be applied with a brush or spray gun. Care must be taken to keep the material off the skin and away from eyes, especially when spraying. Rubber gloves and some form of eye protection should be worn. Fence posts can be protected against decay by soaking them in creosote.

Paint, stain and varnish are common decorative materials for timber. Apart from an occasional job, these preservatives will have infrequent use in the farm workshop.

Timber must be dry before it is stained or painted. The surface should be rubbed down and dust must be wiped off. New timber should be treated with a knotting solution to seal end grain and knots. When this is dry, a wood priming paint can be applied, followed by a suitable undercoat and then one or two coats of gloss finish. The surface should be lightly rubbed down and dusted between each coat.

Where surface finish is not important, timber can be protected from the weather and from decay with various preparations such as bitumen-based paint and preservatives which control fungus and insect attack.

THINGS TO DO

1. Look at a selection of abrasive sheets including emery cloth, wet-and-dry paper and aluminium oxide paper. Compare the various grades and grits by looking at them and using them.
2. Use a pressure washer, remembering to keep the water away from electrical equipment on tractors. Find out what attachments and accessories can be used with a pressure washer.
3. Always mix paint thoroughly before use.
4. Clean paint brushes after use and store them dry. Make sure that when you replace a lid on a paint tin, it is an airtight fit.
5. Remember that air receiver tanks on air compressors should be drained of water at regular intervals.

QUESTIONS

1. State the main causes of corrosion of iron and steel.
2. What is a de-watering fluid? Give an example of its use.
3. Describe a method of removing a chuck from an electric drill.
4. Name four wood preservatives.
5. What precautions should be taken when using an electric drill with a wire brush or sanding disc?

Chapter 7

Farm Plumbing

MAINTENANCE AND REPAIR of the farm water supply requires some basic knowledge of plumbing, a few specialist tools and a small stock of fittings, ready at hand for any emergency repairs or extensions to an existing system. You may find water pipe made of lead, steel, copper and polythene, and it will be useful to have a few fittings suitable for the repair of the last three pipe materials. Any installation involving lead pipe will be better replaced with modern materials and the lead sold to the local scrap merchant.

TOOLS

Most of the tools used for plumbing will be part of the basic farm toolkit. Copper and polythene (Alkathene) installations will require no special tools other than a hacksaw and a spanner or pipe grips. It may be necessary to bend copper pipe from time to time. This can be done with a pipe-bending spring or a more expensive bending machine.

Steel water pipe must be threaded before it can be joined. There is a range of connectors suitable for this work.

Vices and Grips

A *metalworking vice* can be used but care must be taken to avoid damage to the pipe when working with copper. A proper pipe vice is better because it grips a much greater surface area of the pipe and there is virtually no risk of damage. A *pipe vice* has vee-shaped jaws, one fixed and the other adjusted with a screw handle. The upper section is hinged and is held in place with a self-locking latch. The vice is opened to allow the pipe into the lower jaw, then the upper jaw is latched back in position, after which the vice is tightened. The latch mechanism allows long lengths of pipe to be placed in the vice with ease. A *pipe vice stand* is a useful piece of equipment which includes a platform and a shelf for

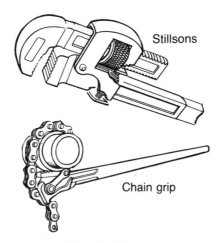

Fig. 64. Pipe grips

tools. The operator stands on the platform while working at the vice. This tool serves as an excellent plumber's portable bench.

Metalwork vices are liable to flatten soft pipe if the jaws are over-tightened. The use of *fibre vice grips* will reduce the risk of damage to the pipe. It would not be too difficult for the mechanic to make a pair of vee-shaped jaws, suitable for gripping pipe, which could be used in a metalworking vice.

The *Stillson wrench* is found in most farm workshops. It is ideal for working with steel water pipe.

Stillsons are made in a variety of sizes. A typical wrench has an overall length of 600 mm (24 in) and can be used to grip pipe up to 90 mm in diameter. Stillsons have a spring-loaded moving jaw which is designed to grip when turned in one direction. They can be used with the jaws above or below the pipe, depending on the position of the pipe and whether it is to be loosened or tightened.

Another type of pipe grip is a *chain wrench*. The chain is wrapped round the pipe and then threaded through an eye at the end of the handle. Both chain and Stillson wrenches should be kept clean and the moving parts lightly oiled. Never use a pipe wrench with worn teeth—it will probably slip. Don't use a pipe wrench which is not really big enough for the job; this can damage the wrench and can slip off the pipe. The risk of damaging soft pipe will be reduced if a piece of cloth is wrapped round the pipe to protect it from the jaws of the grips.

Pipe Cutters

The *hacksaw* is the usual pipe-cutting tool. Remember that most water pipe has a thin wall and should be sawn with a fine blade. On the other hand polythene pipe should be sawn with a coarse blade; some prefer to cut this material with a sharp knife. After the pipe has been cut it should be cleaned, inside and out, with a suitable file.

Roller pipe cutters are often used by plumbers. The smaller tube cutter is used for soft metal pipe such as copper. A heavy pattern pipe

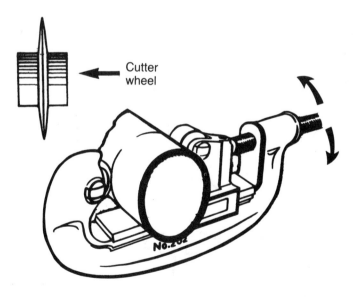

Cutter wheel

Fig. 65. Pipe cutters

cutter is needed for working with steel pipe. One type of pipe cutter has three hard steel cutting discs and is useful in positions where the cutter cannot be rotated right round the pipe. A second type of pipe cutter has two supporting rollers and one cutting wheel. This tool must be rotated round the pipe. The single cutting wheel is held in a fixed jaw and the rollers (or the pair of cutters) are brought into contact with the pipe by means of a screw handle.

A tube cutter is a handy lightweight tool suitable for copper and other soft metal tube up to 30 mm in diameter. The heavier pipe cutter will, according to size, cut steel pipe up to 100 mm inside diameter (bore).

To cut pipe with a roller cutter place it over the work with the two rollers held firmly against the pipe. Turn the screw handle to adjust the cutting wheel until it bites into the pipe. At this point rotate the tool, at the same time gradually tightening the cutting wheel until the pipe is cut through. Care must be taken to keep the cutter square on the pipe. After use, store the cutter with the jaws closed and keep the moving parts lightly oiled.

Tank Cutters

When fixing a ball valve or similar fitting in a tank, it will be necessary to cut a large-diameter hole. This can be done by drilling a ring of small holes almost on the circumference of the required hole size. Once the bulk of the metal has been removed, final shaping is done with chisel and file. A tank cutter, or hole saw, will do this job faster and more accurately. There are several sizes of hole saw, a typical range will cut holes from 16 to 100 mm ($\frac{5}{8}$ to 4 in) in diameter.

Fig. 66. Hole saw

The hole saw incorporates a twist drill. This makes a pilot hole to guide the saw and ensure the hole us cut in the correct position.

Mark the centre point of the hole with a centre punch, then, after fitting the hole saw in an electric drill, make the pilot hole. Hold the saw teeth firmly against the metal while cutting the hole. Take extra care when the work nears completion to ensure the shape of the hole is not damaged when the saw teeth break through the metal.

PIPE BENDING

Steel pipe will normally be installed is straight runs or with a slight curve. Elbows and bends are used to make sharp changes of direction. Copper pipe is easy to bend but care must be taken to avoid kinking the pipe. A bending spring makes it possible to bend copper pipe without damaging the shape of the pipe section.

A bending spring is a tough, close-coiled spring, long enough to be pushed into a pipe to the point where a bend is required. The spring has an eye at one end for a piece of wire or strong cord. Bending springs for both 15 and 22 mm ($\frac{1}{2}$ and $\frac{3}{4}$ in) copper pipe can be obtained from tool shops.

To bend a piece of copper pipe, push the bending spring into the required position, remembering to put a cord through the eye of the spring to facilitate removal when the bend is completed. Hold the pipe against your knee, just below the kneecap, and exert a steady pressure until the required shape is obtained. Bend the pipe a little at a time, checking the angle as you proceed. It may be found easier to withdraw the bending spring if the pipe is bent slightly too much and then returned to the correct angle before attempting to withdraw it. A simple pipe bender can be made in the workshop. Drill a hole, large enough for the pipe, in a piece of 50 mm × 50 mm timber. Chamfer the edge of the hole. Fill the pipe with sand, put it in the hole and bend to the required shape.

Specialist pipe-bending machines are used by plumbers. They give very fast and accurate pipe bending. This equipment can hardly be justified for the farm workshop but can be hired for short periods at a low cost from tool-hire shops.

PIPE DIES

Steel water pipe must be threaded before two pieces can be joined. This type of pipe is measured by its nominal bore (inside diameter): $\frac{1}{2}$ in and $\frac{3}{4}$ in are common sizes. The pipe may be galvanised or ordinary black steel.

The size of pipe threads and pipe dies is based on the nominal bore diameter. A 1 in bore pipe has an outside diameter of 1·31 in. The bore is described as nominal because it can vary slightly due to small differences in the wall thickness.

The simple type of pipe die is similar to that used for threading round bar. However, the thread pattern is different, British Standard Pipe thread (BSP) being used (see page 89). Select the correct size of die and place it with the tapered, leading face, downwards in the die holder. Secure the die and adjust it with the small set screws in the same way as described on page 53. Many pipe die holders have a guide on one side which is placed over the pipe to help keep it square when starting a new thread. Cut the thread in the same way as described for threading a round bar; use plenty of lubricant. It is easier to make a good thread if the pipe is cut square.

Table 22. Dimensions of BSP thread

Nominal bore—inches	$\frac{1}{4}$	$\frac{3}{8}$	$\frac{1}{2}$	$\frac{5}{8}$	$\frac{3}{4}$	1	$1\frac{1}{2}$
Outside diameter—inches	0·518	0·656	0·825	0·902	1·041	1·65	1·882
Threads per inch	19	19	14	14	14	11	11

A more expensive type of pipe die consists of a ratchet holder with two handles and a four-piece set of thread cutters. Each cutter is numbered 1 to 4 and must be placed in the slot, marked with the same number, in the holder. After correct assembly, the cutters are locked in position. The die stock (holder) can be adjusted to suit different sizes of pipe. The same cutters can be used for threading any diameter pipe with the same number of threads per inch. For changes in tpi a different set of cutters must be used.

Test the setting of the pipe dies with a spare length of pipe to make sure the thread is cut deep enough. Pipe dies cut a slightly tapered thread. The trial thread should run into a threaded female socket for about four turns without the use of pipe grips. If the pipe is very loose, the thread is too deep. Don't cut too much thread when joining pipe; the thread length should be the same as the thread diameter.

There is no need to turn the die backwards when using this type of die because there is plenty of room in the holder for the metal chips to get away from the cutter teeth. The ratchet mechanism can be used with either one or two handles. With only one handle fitted, the die can be used in a very confined space. Use plenty of lubricant.

Always clean the dies after use. Take them to pieces, remove all traces of metal chips (swarf), wipe with an oily rag, reassemble and store in a safe place.

When assembling the pipework, apply any sealant used to the pipe's male thread, not to the female thread. This will keep the sealant away from the water so there will not be any contamination.

There are BSP taps for cutting internal threads. They have few uses on the farm and a set of BSP taps would be difficult to justify. It is best to buy a tap of the required size, should the need arise.

Other Plumbing Tools

Files, both flat and round, will be needed for trimming rough edges after pipe has been sawn to length.

Steel wool, or fine *emery cloth*, is used to clean copper pipe in preparation for making soldered joints.

A *blowtorch* is required to provide heat when making soldered joints. A small butane torch with a disposable gas cylinder will be adequate for occasional plumbing, whereas a torch attached to a larger, rechargeable gas cylinder would be better for the busy plumber. The paraffin type of blowlamp is another type of heating torch suitable for this work.

An *asbestos pad* or small *asbestos blanket* should be obtained to protect surrounding areas when making a soldered joint with a blow-torch.

Finally, a *steel tape* and a *rule* will be needed to ensure accurate work. Remember the golden rule—measure twice and cut once!

PIPE FITTINGS

There is a vast range of pipe fittings on the market. They are made for all types of water pipe and it is also possible to obtain fittings suitable for changing from one type of water pipe to another. In this way, polythene, for example, can be converted to copper fittings or to steel fittings with the aid of a single connector.

Steel water fittings are threaded, so once the pipe has been threaded all that remains is to connect the parts together to obtain a watertight joint. Sealing compounds or tape can be used to ensure a leakproof joint.

PLUMBING WITH COPPER PIPE

There are two types of joint for copper pipe. Compression joints are tightened with a spanner and can be dismantled when the need arises. Capillary joints are more permanent as they are soldered. The joint has a ring of solder at each end which is melted with a blowlamp to seal it.

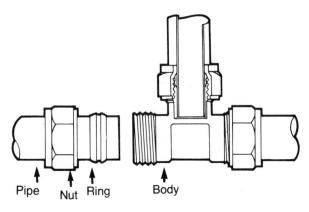

Fig. 67. Compression joint

Compression fittings have a central body with a male thread and a cap nut at each end. An olive, or compression ring, is placed over the pipe; the joint is assembled and the cap nuts tightened by hand. PTFE tape or a non-toxic plumber's sealing compound can be put on the threads to help ensure a watertight joint. The final task in making a compression joint is to tighten the cap nuts with a spanner. This will cause the compression rings to bite into the pipe.

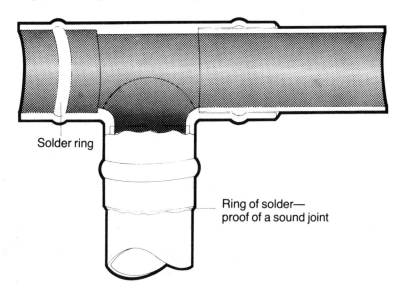

Fig. 68. Capillary joint

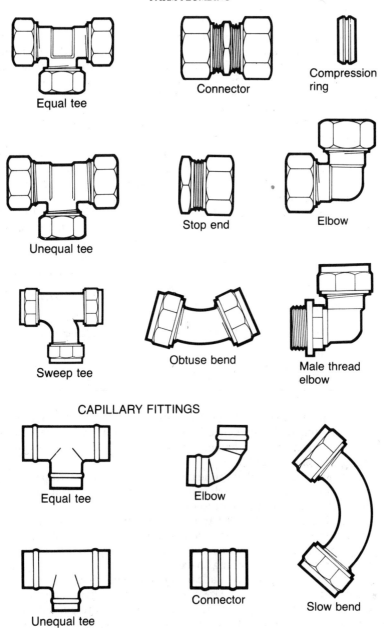

Equal tee

Connector

Compression ring

Unequal tee

Stop end

Elbow

Sweep tee

Obtuse bend

Male thread elbow

CAPILLARY FITTINGS

Equal tee

Elbow

Unequal tee

Connector

Slow bend

Fig. 69. Common pipe fittings

Before the joint is assembled, the ends of the pipe must be saw
square and all rough edges removed with a file.

Capillary joints are very simple; they are cheaper and neater than
compression joint. The joint is made by cutting the pipe ends square an
trimming the rough edges with a file. The ends of the pipe and the insid
of the connector must be cleaned with steel wool or fine glasspaper. /
special flux is applied to the ends of the pipe and then the joint can b
assembled. Make sure that the ends of the pipe are hard against th
stops inside the connector. Some straight connectors do not have stop
for the pipe, which allows the joint to be assembled in a position wher
an ordinary connector could not be used. The connector can be slippe
completely on to one piece of pipe if required; this can be very usefu
when repairing a damaged or burst pipe.

When the joint has been assembled, heat from a blowtorch is used t
melt the solder ring. As soon as solder appears at the ends of th

Table 23. Common sizes of copper water pipe

| Pipe size | | Conversion from imperial to metric |
imperial	metric	
$\frac{1}{2}$ in	15 mm	fittings are interchangeable
$\frac{3}{4}$ in	22 mm	special adaptor required
1 in	28 mm	fittings are interchangeable

connector, remove the heat source and allow the joint to cool. A small
asbestos mat or blanket placed behind the joint will protect the surrounding area from the flame. When the joint is set, wipe away excess
flux with a piece of cloth.

If you require to seal only one end of a capillary joint, wrap a wet cloth
around the solder ring which is to be left free. Apply heat to the other
ring and watch for the solder to run.

The pipe must be free of water when making a soldered joint. If water
is present in the pipe it will be almost impossible to melt the solder. This
problem will not occur with a new installation but can well happen when
making a repair or extending an existing system.

Copper pipe fittings are made in many shapes and sizes. Adaptors are
made to convert from one size to another and also to change from one
type of pipe material to another sort—e.g. copper to polythene. There
are adaptors to convert from compression to capillary fittings too.

Copper pipe was, until recently, made in imperial sizes, e.g. $\frac{1}{2}$, $\frac{3}{4}$ and 1
in outside diameter. Metric sizes are now manufactured. The size of

copper pipe refers to the outside diameter of the tube. This must not be confused with steel pipe where size relates to the diameter of the bore.

PLUMBING WITH PLASTIC PIPE

Polythene pipe, more familiar under its trade name of Alkathene, is in common use for farm plumbing. It is a non-corrosive, flexible pipe suitable for use in both above- and below-ground installations.

Polythene pipe can be joined with compression fittings similar to those used for copper pipe. The range of fittings is not so large because

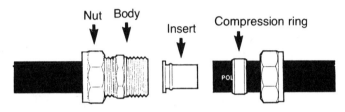

Fig. 70. Polythene pipe connector

the pipe can be bent to meet most requirements. Connectors, tees and elbows will be needed when connecting to existing pipework or fitting extensions.

It is important to cut the ends as square as possible when making a joint, using a hacksaw or sharp knife. The cut ends are strengthened with copper inserts which are pushed into the pipe before the joint is assembled. As there are several types of polythene pipe, it is necessary to check that the correct insert is used. PTFE tape or a non-toxic sealing compound can be used to help ensure a watertight joint. Once assembled, the joint should be tightened as much as possible by hand. A further couple of turns with a spanner will complete the job. Similar to the compression joint for copper pipe, the effect of tightening the cap nut is to force the compression rings into the surface of the pipe.

In cold weather, the pipe can be softened by holding the end in hot water, a help when you are fitting the insert in the pipe.

PVC (polyvinyl chloride) is used for some water systems, mainly for rainwater and waste disposal installations. It may be connected with special couplings which have rubber seals or by solvent welding. In the latter process a highly inflammable solvent is used as a cement to join two pieces of pipe.

TAPS

There are two basic types of tap. A *draw-off tap* has a free outlet and a *stoptap*, or *stopcock*, is used to control the flow of water in a pipe.

A draw-off tap may be a bib tap or a pillar tap. A bib tap is fitted to a wall or post and has a horizontal water entry. A pillar tap is used for wash basins and sinks, and has a vertical water inlet. Taps are made of brass or steel, common sizes being $\frac{1}{2}$, $\frac{3}{4}$ and 1 inch.

Dripping taps cause annoyance and waste water. A new tap washer usually solves the problem. The washer is fitted at the bottom of the tap spindle and is quite easy to replace. If the washer is not the cause, suspect the tap seating. A simple tool can be obtained for re-cutting tap seats.

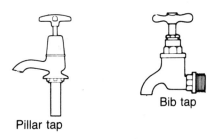

Bib tap

Pillar tap

Fig. 71. Taps

Turn off the water supply before fitting a new tap washer. Remove the tap handle and cover then undo the retaining nut on the tap body. This will release the spindle which can be withdrawn from the tap. The washer is held on the jumper. Fit a new washer, avoid overtightening the jumper nut as this will distort the washer. Reassemble the tap, turn on the water and check for leaks.

Water leaking from the spindle cover indicates that the spindle gland packing is faulty. This can often be cured by tightening the gland nut slightly. If this does not solve the problem, dismantle the tap and replace the packing with soft string. Wind three or four turns of soft string, smeared with tallow or Vaseline, round the tap spindle. Reassemble the tap, tightening the gland nut carefully. Turn on the stopcock and check for leaks.

Stopcocks are used to shut off the water to a complete installation or to isolate part of the system. Gate valves have a screw-operated disc

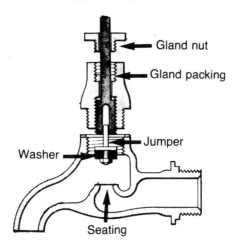

Fig. 72. Working parts of a tap

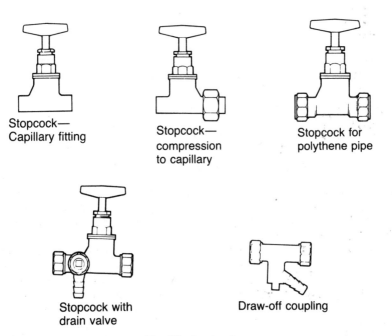

Fig. 73. Stopcocks

which is raised or lowered in the valve body to control the flow. Another type of stopcock allows the water to flow in only one direction, thus stopping water returning to the mains supply from a house or farm installation. An arrow on the body of the stopcock indicates the direction of flow. Fit the stopcock with the arrow pointing in the direction of the water flow.

Some stopcocks have a drain valve, used to drain a water system in readiness for repairs.

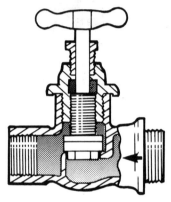

Fig. 74. Working parts of a stop tap

Bib and pillar taps have a male thread for connecting to the pipework. Stopcocks are made with threaded, soldered (capillary) or compression joints.

BALL VALVES

The flow of water into a storage tank or drinking trough can be automatically controlled with a ball valve. It can also be used to adjust the level of water in the tank or trough. A circular metal or plastic float, supported by an arm, operates a valve at the water inlet point. There are several types of valve, the most common being the piston, or plunger valve (see fig. 75).

When the float rises with the water level, the arm moves the plunger into contact with the valve seating. There is a washer at the end of the plunger which is forced against the valve seat by the pressure of the float. When the water level falls, the float drops and allows more water to flow into the tank. The plunger washer may harden, or perish, with use. When this happens, the ball valve must be dismantled and a new washer fitted. The old washer is removed by taking the float and arm off

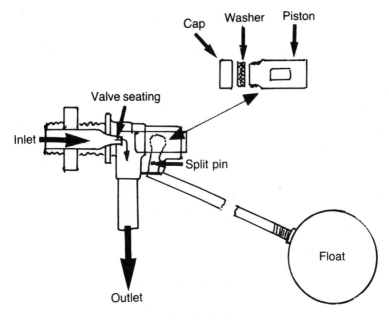

Fig. 75. Ball valve

the valve by withdrawing the split pin. This will release the plunger. It may be necessary on some ball valves to unscrew the end cap on the plunger body. Fit a new washer and reassemble. The split pin is made of brass and can usually be reused; it should only be opened sufficiently to keep it in place.

Other types of ball valve have a diaphragm valve. A rubber diaphragm, or disc, is held against the inlet by a plunger operated through the float. When the water level drops, the diaphragm moves away from the valve seat allowing water to enter the tank. The diaphragm can be replaced when faulty. The method of replacement is similar to that for a plunger type ball valve.

There are ball valves for both high- and low-pressure installations, and it is important to use the correct type. Ball valves directly connected to the mains need a high-pressure valve. The low-pressure valve has a larger orifice (hole) through which the water flows when the valve is open. This type is used for troughs, etc., supplied from a header tank.

The water level in a tank or trough is adjusted by bending the float arm until the required level is obtained; some ball valves have an adjusting screw to alter this level. A faulty ball valve may not completely cut off the flow, and for this reason storage tanks should have an overflow pipe to prevent flooding.

A common problem with ball valves is the build-up of limescale on the moving parts. In severe cases, it can seize completely. All moving parts of a ball valve should be checked from time to time and any trace of limescale removed. Complete failure is usually caused by a punctured float. Replacement is the only remedy; a plastic bag placed over the punctured float will give a temporary cure.

AUTOMATIC DRINKERS

Field troughs, drinking bowls and nipple drinkers have an automatic control which includes a valve seat and washer. With constant use, the washer will wear, or perish, and should be replaced.

Field troughs have a standard type of ball valve. It is important to protect the valve assembly from damage by stock. Keep the guard in place. Cattle bowls have a tongue-operated flap or a small ball valve. Nipple pig drinkers have a plunger, pushed in by the animal's nose. This allows water to flow into a bowl or trough. The bite drinker releases water when the animal grips the nipple with its teeth.

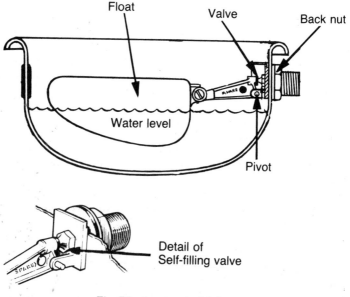

Fig. 76. Automatic drinker

INSTALLING PIPEWORK

Plan the layout of the system and make a full list of the materials required. The list should include pipe, fittings, clips, jointing compound, etc. Your order for pipe and fittings should specify:

- Type and size of pipe.
- Type of joint, i.e. capillary, compression or threaded. Indicate if male or female threads are required.
- The quantity of each type of fitting, e.g. elbows, tees, stopcocks. Allow one or two spares.
- Connectors and elbows with unequal ends should be ordered with the larger size first. For unequal tees, state the size of the pipe run end first, followed by the size for continuing the run and lastly, the size of the branch outlet, e.g. $28 \times 22 \times 15$; $22 \times 22 \times 15$. In both examples, the 15 mm outlet is for the branch pipe. Give precise specifications for fittings which have different connections, e.g. 15 mm copper to $\frac{1}{2}$ in BSP.

Use pipe with a sufficiently large diameter for the job. If further extensions are planned, provide for them by using suitable diameter pipe. Leave a small extension to the system with a stop end or plug ready for future connections.

Support the pipe runs properly. Copper pipe up to 28 mm bore needs a clip at a maximum spacing of 2 m for horizontal runs and 2·5 m for vertical work. Polythene pipe should be clipped at 500 mm spacing for horizontal runs and 750 mm for vertical pipe. Clips should be spaced at similar intervals to copper when securing steel pipe.

Where practical, keep pipework away from outside walls and exposed positions. If this is not possible, include some pipe lagging material on your shopping list.

Copper and polythene pipe can be bent to an angle of up to 90°. It is better to use an elbow for sharp corners, particularly when it is important to keep the pipe close to the wall. An elbow must be used for steel pipe.

Allow for movement of pipes which pass through a wall by placing a short piece of pipe of larger diameter in the wall to act as a sleeve.

Measure the required length of pipe with care. Remember to allow for the fact that the pipe will be held away from the wall by the pipe clips when finally installed. Make allowance in the measurements for the pipe fittings too. Pipe is expensive, so check the measurement before cutting it. Mistakes can be remedied by joining two pieces of pipe but this is a waste of time and materials.

Take care when tightening pipe connections. Compression fittings should be tightened as far as possible by hand, followed by up to one turn with a spanner for copper pipe fittings and about 1½ turns for polythene pipe fittings. It is better to tighten a joint a little more if it weeps; if it is overtightened, the joint may be distorted and this can cause a leak.

FROST PROTECTION

Farm water installations often have no protection from frost. Water pipes in unheated buildings should be lagged to reduce the risk of a burst. There are several materials suitable for lagging pipes including sacking and felt. Lagged pipes in farm buildings, especially where livestock are housed, should be protected from the stock by wire mesh or by being boxed in with timber. Split polystyrene or foam rubber tubing can be placed over the pipes and held in position with tape. Again, this material must be protected from attack by inquisitive livestock.

Very low-power heating cables can be wrapped round water pipes in exposed positions. A thermostatic control will give frost protection with no risk of a burst pipe, except during a power cut.

Drinking troughs and outside taps should either be drained or given the best possible protection during the winter. Where possible, draining the water provides the surest and cheapest form of protection.

Storage tanks should be protected from frost. Make sure the lagging material is safe from vermin attack and don't lag under a loft tank, it will act as a barrier to any heat rising from below.

Burst Pipes

When water freezes, its volume increases. The tell-tale drip of a burst pipe will only appear when the thaw sets in. Frozen pipes in a farm building can be thawed out if the problem is located in time. Depending on the position of the frozen pipe, one or more of the following remedies can be tried.

- Pour boiling water over the frozen area—this usually works with a frozen tap.
- Cloths, soaked in hot water and then wrung out before placing on the frozen pipe will sometimes do the trick.
- Direct a blast of hot air from a fan heater or a hair drier on to the affected area.
- On steel pipe, gentle heat from a small blowtorch can be used. A blowtorch must not be used in a position where there is a risk of causing a fire, and any pipe lagging must be removed first. Keep a can of water handy in case of an emergency.

Compression fittings on copper or polythene pipes are the weak point in the system, and sometimes the frozen water will push the connection apart without further damage. When this happens, thaw the pipe and re-make the joint. Burst copper pipes will need a new section of pipe so cut out the damaged area and replace it in the normal way. In some cases it will not be possible to use a standard capillary joint to make the repair. A slip connector should be used; this has no pipe stops and can be pushed fully on to one piece of pipe and then slipped back over the other piece when both pipes are in their correct position.

Steel pipe with threaded connectors presents a different problem. When a burst occurs in a run of pipe, it is not possible to cut out the damaged section and replace it with new pipe and two connectors. This method can only be used if much of the installation is dismantled. A new piece of pipe cannot be put into a length of pipe where the burst occurred because all pipe threads are right handed, tightening one connection will cause the next one to come undone.

This problem can be overcome by using either a special coupling or a running joint.

A coupling has three main parts (see fig. 77). The two half joints (*a*)

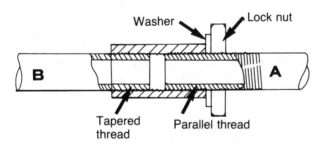

RUNNING JOINT

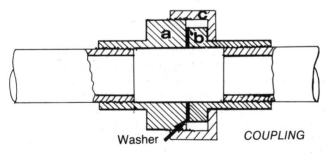

Fig. 77. Pipe couplings

and (b) are tightened on to threaded pipe ends. The nut (c) clamps the two half joints together; the washer provides a water-tight seal.

A running joint consists of a connector, a back nut and a washer. The diagram shows pipe A with a parallel thread of a length slightly greater than the connector. Pipe B has a much shorter, tapered thread. The running joint is assembled by running the backnut, washer and connector fully on to pipe A. The connector is then screwed back on to pipe B and tightened. The joint is completed by tightening the back nut up to the connector. For both couplings, the addition of some sealing compound on the male threads will help to make the joint leakproof.

A temporary repair could be made to a burst pipe with a short length of hosepipe and a couple of hose clips. Cut out the damaged section of pipe, slip the hosepipe complete with clips on to the two cut ends and tighten the clips. This should be replaced with a permanent repair as soon as possible.

A very slight leak can sometimes be sealed with some PTFE tape wrapped round the pipe, over the hole. Make sure that the pipe surface is really clean before wrapping the tape.

THINGS TO DO

1. Look for the specialist plumbing tools mentioned in this chapter. Dismantle and reassemble a set of adjustable pipe dies. Take careful note of the position of each thread cutter in the holder.
2. Learn the names of the various types of pipe fitting.
3. Watch someone making a pipe joint. If possible, practise this skill yourself.
4. Fit a new washer to a tap.
5. Dismantle a ball valve, study its construction, then reassemble the unit.

QUESTIONS

1. Why is the size, or bore, of a pipe described as nominal?
2. What is a capillary joint? Describe the procedure for joining two pieces of copper pipe with a capillary type connector.
3. Describe three methods suitable for thawing a frozen pipe.
4. What is a running joint?
5. List materials which can be used for lagging water pipes. What precautions should be taken when lagging a pipe in a livestock building?

Chapter 8

Working with Metal

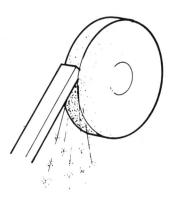

METAL PARTS can be joined with nuts and bolts, rivets or with a welder. Earlier chapters deal with welding techniques and the types of nut and bolt.

RIVETING

This is a simple but effective way of permanently joining two pieces of metal or other materials. Combine harvester knife sections, for example, are fixed to the knife back with rivets. Clutch and brake linings are often riveted to the clutch plate or brake shoe. Sheet metal can be riveted on to its supporting framework. Blacksmith's tongs are held together with a rivet which provides a permanent, movable joint.

The main types of rivet are described on page 91; they are usually made from steel, brass, aluminium and copper. The type of rivet used will depend on the form of joint and its purpose. Where the head must be level with the surface of the metal, a countersunk rivet is used.

Fitting Knife Sections

Old combine harvester, mower or hedge trimmer sections must be removed from the knife and the knife back straightened on an anvil if necessary. The old rivets can be removed by grinding off the heads, cutting them off with a chisel or shearing them off in a vice (see fig. 12). Worn sections can be removed quickly by placing them in a slightly open vice with the knife back resting on the inner vice jaw. The vice should be adjusted so that the sections can just move in the jaws. Strike the back of the section with a smart hammer blow at a point just above each rivet. With a little practice, one hammer blow will shear each rivet. Don't do this job close to a window and, for preference, use an old vice. After the sections have been removed, punch the rivets from the knife back. This method cannot be used if the back of the section is flush with the knife back. Countersunk rivets can be removed by drilling out the rivet head and then driving out the remainder of the rivet with a hammer and punch.

Select new rivets of the correct size and gauge (diameter) for the replacement knife sections. If the rivet is too short, there will be little strength in the final joint. The rivet will bend, rather than swell properly, if it is too long. As a guide, the length of the rivet shank left for riveting over should be equivalent to $1\frac{1}{4}$ times the rivet diameter; e.g., a 4 mm diameter rivet should have 5 mm left for riveting over.

For round-head rivets, place a small riveting anvil in a vice to support the head of the rivet. This tool is not required for flat-head rivets. Put a rivet in the hole in the knife back and the section. Close the two parts with a rivet set (see fig. 9) then swell the rivet with a hammer. Line up the second pair of holes in the knife back and section, use the set and then swell the rivet. Finally, complete the job with a rivet snap or the ball end of a ball-pein hammer.

Two pieces of metal which are to be riveted should first be clamped together in the correct position. Drill one hole, slightly bigger than the diameter of the chosen rivet. Place the rivet in the hole, swell it and finish the job with a snap. Drill at least two more holes with the clamp still in place and rivet the parts together. Remove the clamp, drill any other holes required and complete the riveting process.

It is important to use a rivet set to ensure the two parts are in close contact. Failure to do this properly may result in a loose joint.

When a rivet is used to form a hinged joint, place a piece of card between the two parts. Fit and tighten the rivet and then remove the card; if necessary it can be burnt away.

Pop rivets are useful for refixing loose sheet metal work, guards, etc. They can be used in places where it is only possible to get at one side of the work. The rivet has a soft metal sleeve with a hard rivet pin in the

1. Using the set
2. Swell the rivet
3. Shape the rivet tail
4. Finish with a rivet snap.

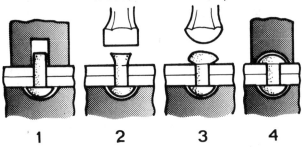

1   **2**   **3**   **4**

Fig. 78. Stages of riveting

centre. The pop riveting gun pulls the rivet pin through the sleeve, expanding it until it is tight in the hole. At that point the pin snaps off with a 'pop'.

Drill holes slightly bigger than the rivet diameter, put a rivet in the gun and then place it in the drilled hole. With the rivet in position, operate the rivet gun lever until the rivet pin snaps off.

FORGING

Iron and steel are much easier to bend when they are hot. Hot forging is the skill of a blacksmith with a coke-fired hearth. Few farm workshops will have this facility. Occasional hot forging can be done with the aid of an oxy-acetylene blowpipe. Bent components can be heated ready for straightening and small items can be made with steel strip or bar.

The basic equipment, other than a forge, consists of an anvil, heavy hammer, tongs and a range of sets, swages, hardies, etc. A round swage is used to draw out or reduce the diameter of a piece of round bar. Sets and hardies are used for cutting hot metal.

A simple forging job is drawing out tines for cultivation equipment. Harrow tines, blunt with use, can be brought to red heat, hammered to a point and returned to service.

The basic rule for successful forgework is to ensure that the iron is hot. Don't let it burn but do wait for it to obtain a good red heat. The colour is easier to see if the heating is done away from direct sunlight.

The anvil must be kept clear of clutter and should be placed on an anvil stand or secured to a good-size hardwood block.

Shafts, tines, etc., made from medium-carbon steel can be straightened with the aid of a forge. However, these parts have been given special heat treatment by the manufacturer to make them hard and tough. If you heat them in a forge to straighten them you will remove this hard, tough property. For this reason, it is better to replace such damaged components. Without the correct heat treatment (difficult to achieve in the farm workshop) to harden and temper a straightened part, it will soon bend when returned to service. Sometimes a slight bend can be straightened cold. A heavy hammer and an anvil or a really solid piece of concrete floor are all the tools you will require.

HOME-MADE TOOLS

Discarded shafts from farm implements make excellent crowbars and pry bars. The ends can be brought to red heat and forged into a point at one end and a flat chisel edge at the other.

The stems of discarded engine valves make excellent taper punches if the valve head is removed and the stem is drawn out; they can also be ground to form a centre punch. Small push rods can be ground to a point to make a scriber. Worn files can be turned into useful scrapers. The removal of fencing staples is simplified with an old cutter bar finger with a sharp point. This is hammered into the staple eye, an action which soon withdraws the staple itself.

With a little practice, you will be able to forge an eye or ring at the end of a piece of rod or strip metal. First, calculate the length of the material needed to form the eye. The circumference of a circle is found by multiplying its diameter by $3 \cdot 142$; for workshop purposes, it will be near enough to multiply by $3 \cdot 2$. Measure off the required length at the end of the rod and make a clear mark with a centre punch. Heat the bar around the mark, using a forge or an oxy-acetylene blowpipe.

Hold the hot metal with tongs and place it on the anvil, lining up the mark on the metal with the edge of the anvil. Hammer the metal downwards to form a right angle. Reheat the end of the bar. Put the heated section above the beak (point) of the anvil with the cold end held upwards. Hammer the hot metal downwards, partly round the beak. Re-heat as necessary, gradually forming the eye round the anvil. When the ring is almost complete, put it on top of the anvil and close the eye. If necessary the eye can be heated once more and reshaped slightly to give an even, well-formed ring. (See fig. 80.)

A few sensible precautions must be taken when working with hot metal.

• Always use tongs. You can make or buy tongs with jaws suitable for holding various sizes of round, square and flat metal.

a. Set for cutting hot metal
b. Anvil
c. The beak of the anvil
d. Punching a hole in hot metal
e. Tongs for flat metal
f. Tongs for round metal

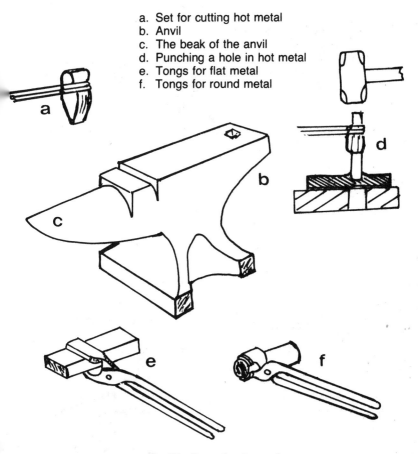

Fig. 79. Some forging tools

- Keep all tools, especially hammers, in good condition.
- Wear suitable protective clothing. This should include boots, or shoes, with steel reinforced toe caps and a leather apron.
- A thick pair of gauntlet gloves should also be available.

A blacksmith's forge has a trough of water alongside, used for cooling hot metal, tongs, etc. Few workshops will have this type of forge but where a small portable forge or oxy-acetylene equipment is used, a supply of cooling water must be provided. A small metal tank or a bucket will be suitable. Avoid the use of containers made from plastic material.

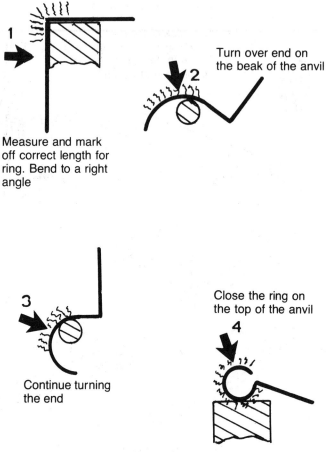

1
Measure and mark off correct length for ring. Bend to a right angle

2 Turn over end on the beak of the anvil

3 Continue turning the end

4 Close the ring on the top of the anvil

Fig. 80. Forging an eye

SHEET METAL WORK

Working with sheet metal is another skill which requires a lot of practice before a proficient standard can be achieved. Simple sheet metal work needs few tools. Marking and measuring equipment, hand snips or a guillotine, a vice and a selection of hammers and mallets will be sufficient. Soft-faced hammers or mallets are used by professionals to obtain a smooth, bruise-free surface.

Methods of cutting sheet metal are described on page 50. Bending this material to make joints or shape guards and containers can be done with

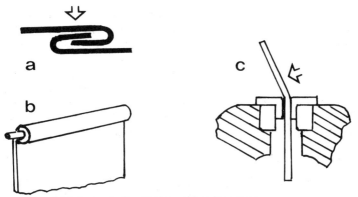

a. Folded joint, ready for closing with a hammer
b. A wired edge
c. Bending sheet metal with two lengths of angle iron held in a vice

Fig. 81. Working with sheet metal

a vice or some cramps and two short lengths of angle iron. Mark the line of the required bend or fold with a scriber. Place the sheet metal between two lengths of angle iron which have already been put in the jaws of a vice. Tighten the vice with the marked line on the sheet metal matched with the corner edge of the angle iron. The sheet can now be bent to any angle up to 90°, using a hammer or mallet.

The sharp edges of a sheet metal container can be made safer and stronger by folding or by wiring the edge. A folded edge is made by turning the metal inwards to a right angle and then folding it completely back on itself. A wired edge is started in the same way. Before folding the metal completely over, a piece of strong wire is placed under the fold. The edge is closed round the wire and the edge of the metal tucked in behind it. A special tinsmith's hammer is best for this work but the handyman should be able to manage with the chisel-shaped end of a cross pein hammer.

Joining Sheet Metal

Two pieces of sheet metal can be joined together by welding, soldering, riveting, screwing or by folding the edges to make a hook joint.

A riveted joint is made with soft rivets or pop rivets. It is usual to make a lap joint with one piece of metal overlapping the other. One or two rows of rivets are used. Corners can be riveted together only if tabs are left for the purpose when marking and cutting the metal. The tabs are folded inwards and riveted to the sides.

Self-tapping screws give a joint which can be taken apart when necessary. Holes, slightly smaller than the self-tapping screw threads, are drilled in the metal. As the screw is tightened, it cuts its own thread in the hole.

A folded joint is similar to that used for food cans. It provides a permanent joint which can be made leakproof with solder. The two edges are folded, one forwards and the other backwards, to form two hooks. The hooked edges are put together and hammered tight. Where required, a folded joint can be cleaned, fluxed and soldered.

Drilling Sheet Metal

Special care is needed when drilling thin sections of metal. Clamp or secure the metal to ensure that it cannot turn with the drill bit as it breaks through the underside of the sheet. Put a piece of timber, hardwood for preference, under the sheet metal. The drill bit will cut into the wood as it pierces the sheet. This is a safer procedure and gives a much better shape to the hole. Small pieces of sheet metal, drilled in a vice with a hand drill, must have a timber backing to reduce the risk of breaking the drill bit, bending the metal or injuring yourself if the drill slips.

The hole shape will be more accurate if the drill bit is sharpened to give a cutting angle slightly greater than the usual 59°.

THINGS TO DO

1. Practise the removal and replacement of knife sections. Use an old knife from a mower or combine harvester.
2. Make a small box with sheet metal. Leave tabs at each corner for riveting. Fold or wire the edges. You could make a number of these boxes for the storage of small spare parts. Empty oil drums, especially the 5 litre size, provide a ready supply of metal.
3. When forging or straightening metal, make sure the iron is hot enough before working the metal.
4. Practise forging an eye at the end of a piece of round bar. Use rod with a diameter of about 10 mm to start with.
5. Always support sheet metal with a piece of wood before drilling a hole in it.

QUESTIONS

1. Name three types of rivet. Give an example of the use of each named type.
2. What is the purpose of a rivet set and a rivet snap?
3. What precautions should be taken when working with hot metal?
4. State four ways which are suitable for joining two pieces of sheet metal.
5. Why are the edges of sheet metal parts sometimes folded or wired?

Chapter 9

General Repair Work

THE MAIN workshop activities include welding, tractor and machinery overhauls together with day-to-day maintenance and repairs. This chapter deals with some of the minor repairs and problems which can occur in the farm workshop.

SEIZED NUTS AND BOLTS

This problem often arises with older equipment, especially if the machines work with the soil or corrosive materials. Heavy-handed mechanics are another cause of sheared off bolts and studs!

Where possible, soak the seized nuts, or other components, with penetrating oil or a home-made mixture of diesel fuel and oil. Sometimes this treatment will loosen the rust sufficiently for the nut to come undone. It may help to release a seized nut if it is tightened a little before attempting to undo it. Do remember to turn the spanner in the right direction. A nut will come undone if it is turned anti-clockwise when you are facing it.

Heat, applied with an oxy-acetylene blowpipe, will often break the rust seal by expanding the nut slightly. Don't use this remedy if there is even the slightest risk of causing a fire. Threads can be stretched to

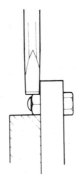

Fig. 82. Cutting through a seized nut

break the rust seal by hammering each face of the nut in turn. When the nut is part of a small assembly, support the underside of the nut on an anvil while hammering the opposite face. If the seized nut is on a machine, hold a weight against the nut while hammering the opposite face. After this treatment, the nut usually comes loose with a spanner.

These methods of freeing a seized nut usually mean that the nut and bolt can be reused after cleaning the threads. Rub some valve-grinding paste on to the threads and then run the nut up and down the bolt a few times. This will usually clean the thread. Wash the paste off with some paraffin before using the nut and bolt. It is better to clean the threads with a thread file, a die or a die nut if you have one of the correct size.

When all other attempts fail, the nut must be cut off with a hacksaw or cold chisel. Use a sharp cold chisel and cut through the nut face. Don't try to cut from the end of the nut. When possible, support the opposite face of the nut with a weight or an anvil if the seized part is portable.

The nut can also be cut off with an oxy-acetylene cutter. This is rather drastic and care must be taken to avoid damage to parts held together by the seized bolt. Don't use this method if there is any risk of causing a fire.

Mechanical nut splitters can be obtained from good tool shops. They are rather expensive and would be difficult to justify in most farm workshops.

BROKEN STUDS

Occasionally, a stud or set screw shears off in a threaded hole. When it breaks above the surface of a component it may be possible to turn the broken piece with a pair of self-grips. If this fails, the stud must be drilled out. The broken end should be brought down to the surface level of the component and the centre of the stud marked with a centre punch. Drill out the stud; make a pilot hole and then use a bit which does not quite touch the female thread in the hole. Then the remaining pieces must be removed. Sometimes, the tang of a file will grip in the hole if the stud is a small one. Where this is the case, you may be able to turn the file and remove the remains of the stud. A taper tap can be used to cut away the old metal and restore the thread. An alternative is to use a tapered stud extractor. It has a left-hand spiral and as it is tightened into the hole, the extractor should turn out the broken thread. This tool will work well provided that the stud has been sheared off through heavy handed use of a spanner; success is less likely if the bolt was seized with rust.

Another type of stud extractor is used for fitting and removing studs during the normal course of repair work, as in the case of cylinder head studs. This tool, which can be used to remove a stud which has sheared off above the surface of the hole, consists of an eccentric serrated disc which grips the shank of the stud against the side of the extractor body. It is turned with a tee handle to remove the stud. The position of the serrated disc is reversed when the tool is used for tightening studs. This type of stud extractor can also be used with socket spanner handles.

DIFFICULT STUDS, SCREWS AND PINS

Tightening a bolt or stud in a confined space often presents a problem; an open-ended, ring or socket spanner may be difficult or impossible to use. This can be solved by cutting a slot for a screwdriver in the head of the bolt or stud before assembly. Once the stud has started in the hole it can be turned with a screwdriver, leaving the last turn of the bolt to be completed, where possible, with a spanner.

Where it is obvious that you will have difficulty during assembly with turning nuts and bolts, put some oil on the threads and run the nut up and down the bolt a few times to make sure it is free.

Small screws and bolts are sometimes difficult to hold when starting them in a hole. Push the screw through a small hole made in a thin strip of card. The screw can then be held over the hole while it is turned with a screwdriver. This method can be used for wood, metal thread and self-tapping screws.

Small nuts, pins, washers, etc., dropped into inaccessible places can be retrieved with a hook bent on the end of a piece of wire or with some thick grease on the end of a screwdriver blade or a piece of thin rod. The lost part will stick to the grease. The blade of a screwdriver sometimes becomes magnetised after working on a magneto. This can be a nuisance but can also be turned to advantage for retrieving small ferrous parts which have dropped into a recess too small for your fingers. You can magnetise a screwdriver by stroking the tip of the blade in one direction with a permanent magnet.

Correct Assembly of Parts

Care must be taken when dismantling a machine to make sure that the parts will be reassembled in the correct order, with no pieces left over! Mark each part, using your own code, to show the relationship of one item to another. When taking small items apart, place them on a clean surface in the order in which they were removed. Reassemble in the reverse order and all should be well. Use containers to hold small items which are so easily lost, especially when a repair job is left for a few days.

For the inexperienced mechanic, a simple sketch showing the order of assembly will provide the necessary information. Instruction manuals and parts lists are available for many farm machines. Providing that you have the correct reference book for the machine under repair, it should be possible to find details about the correct order of assembly.

BEARINGS AND BUSHES

Bushes and the outer races of taper roller bearings can be difficult to remove from their housings. Sometimes they can be pressed out with the aid of a vice or they can be driven out with a hammer and punch. It is better to drive out a bush with a special removing tool which you can make (see fig. 83B). The removing tool should be a good fit in the bush and have a shoulder slightly smaller than the outside diameter. Take special care when removing a bush from a casting. It may help to warm an aluminium casting.

Small-diameter bushes can be removed by cutting a thread in the bush. A bolt (a) with a long thread, a nut to fit it, a short piece of pipe (b) and a large washer (c) are assembled as shown in fig. 83A. The nut (d) is turned slowly down the bolt. This action will withdraw the bush from the hole in most cases.

A bush in a through hole can be removed by splitting it along its length. Use a hacksaw or a broken hacksaw blade in a pad handle. Once split, the bush can be punched out.

The outer race of a taper roller bearing can normally be punched out. There are sometimes cutaway sections in the housing, which may be hidden with grease. These cutaway sections facilitate the use of a punch for removal of the bearing. Stubborn races may require some help. One method is to run a bead of electric weld on the taper face of the race. The

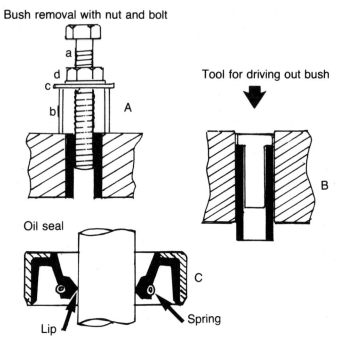

Fig. 83. Working with bearings and seals

heat from the weld will usually free it sufficiently so that it can be punched out.

Fitting Bearings and Bushes

New bearings and bushes must be fitted carefully to avoid damaging them. Place a flat piece of metal, wider than the bearing itself, on top of it and hammer the bearing home. Make sure that it remains square as it is driven into the housing. Bearings can be pressed into place too. Use a hand or hydraulic press or a vice. Protect the parts with two pieces of wood or some fibre vice grips. Bushes can be pressed into place but it is likely that the shape of the bush will be distorted slightly. Once fitted, restore the bush to the correct diameter with a reamer. A twist drill would do this job for very small bushes. Do this work with care as the diameter of the bush must not be enlarged beyond its original size. If the bush has an oil hole, make sure that it is lined up with the hole in the housing.

Taper bearing races can be pressed into their housings or driven into place with a soft-faced hammer. Take care to keep the race square while hammering it into the housing. Some centre punch marks will hold a bearing which turns on its shaft. Thread locking adhesive can be used if a bearing is loose.

Ball and roller bearings can be pressed on to a shaft or into a housing. Never apply force to the unsupported part of the bearing. Apply force to the outer race if the bearing is fitted in a housing and to the inner race if it is to be driven on to a shaft.

Power Take-off Shaft Bearings

Power shaft universal joint bearings have needle roller bearings held in position with circlips. They have dust seals to protect the bearing needles from grit. A new set of bearings must be fitted when the old ones are worn.

Removal will be easier if the circlips are taken off and the area around the housings is cleaned thoroughly.

Sometimes the bearing cups can be removed by hammering the joint at the position shown in fig. 84. With the circlips removed, the hammer blows will usually jar the bearing cups out of their housings.

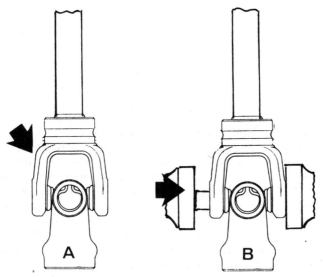

A. Strike yoke with hammer to jar bearing cups from yoke
B. Close vice jaws to press cups partly out of yoke

Fig. 84. Removal of power shaft bearings

When this does not work a vice can be used. Open the jaws wide enough to take the joint and a short piece of round bar slightly smaller than the diameter of the bearing cup (see fig. 84). Tighten the vice jaws, this will push the opposite cup slightly out of its housing until it becomes level with the vice jaw. Turn the unit round in the vice and push the cups in the opposite direction. This should free both cups sufficiently to allow them to be punched out. Use a large diameter punch; it should be a close fit in the housing. Repeat the procedure for the other pair of bearing cups.

Clean the bearing housings, remove any burrs and then fit the replacement crosspiece complete with a new set of seals. Check that the grease nipple in the crosspiece is in the right position. Fit an opposite pair of needle cups in the housings and line them up with the crosspiece. Press the cups into the housings with a vice. Repeat the procedure for the other pair of cups. Use a short piece of round bar to press the cups fully home. Fit a circlip to hold the first cup of each pair in position while you press home the second cup.

If a problem is experienced with needles dropping from the cups during assembly, a light smear of grease on the needles will help to hold them in position.

The bearing should be lubricated before use.

SEALS

Seals are used to retain oil and grease in a bearing or to keep dust and grit out of a bearing. Rubber 'O' rings and felt seals will deteriorate with age and will need replacement. Careful fitting will ensure a long, trouble-free life. The other common type of seal consists of a metal case with a circular tensioning spring and a sealing ring of leather or a synthetic material. The spring holds the sealing ring against the shaft. These seals may also be used to retain oil in a housing or restrict the entry of dirt.

Before a new seal is fitted, check that the shaft and housing are clean and free from rough or sharp edges. A light smear of oil will help with assembly. Fit the seal with the lip facing inwards towards the lubricant. If it is a dust seal, the lip should face outwards.

Make a note of the way the old seal was fitted before you take it out. This will ensure that the replacement is fitted correctly. Press the new seal carefully into the housing, or fit it with a soft hammer. Make sure that the seal is square in the housing during the early stages of fitting.

SHARPENING

Cutting edges of knives and blades on farm equipment will require sharpening from time to time. The mechanic may use, at his choice, a bench or portable grinder, a file or an oilstone.

The sharpest edge will be obtained when it is filed or trimmed from the cutting edge backwards. This means that the operator must stand in front of the knife. This is perfectly safe for the experienced hand but the beginner should take care.

A mower knife may be sharpened with a portable grinder or a file. Don't forget to wear goggles when grinding. Special care is needed when filing knife sections while standing in front of a knife, it is very easy to cut a finger. The beginner may be safer standing behind the knife and filing towards the edge, although the edge may not be quite so keen.

Clamp the knife to a trestle or grip it in a vice with the sections in a horizontal position. Make sure to maintain the correct bevel on the cutting edges.

The ledger plates—the cutting edges on the fingers—must be sharp too. Sharpen them periodically with an angle grinder disc and maintain a bevel angle of approximately 75°.

Flails should be sharpened with a grinder. It is important to keep the cutting edge at the correct angle—use a new flail as a guide.

VEE-BELT DRIVES

Many machines have one or more vee-belt drives. Spare vee-belts should be hung up to help them maintain the correct shape during storage. A label tied on to each belt with information about which machine it fits can save time at busy periods.

Always replace a multiple vee-belt drive system with a complete set of new belts. If one belt breaks, the whole set should be replaced. When one belt in a three-belt drive breaks, the old belts will be stretched compared with the new one and only the new belt would transmit power.

A vee-belt drives through contact between the sides of the belt and the pulley. A belt which runs at the bottom of the pulley is useless. This will happen when the belt has worn or stretched badly or if it is the wrong size of belt for the pulley.

There are several sizes of vee-belt with varying widths, thicknesses and angles. When buying a new belt, make sure that it is the correct length and has the right cross-sectional area.

Correct belt tension is important: a slack belt will slip, causing overheating and rapid wear, and it will not transmit full power. An overtensioned belt will put an undue load on the pulley bearings. this causes rapid wear. Belt tension is checked by measuring the amount of movement (flex) midway along the longest free length of the belt.

The maximum flex, or deflection, in a vee-belt drive should be 16 mm for every metre of belt length between the pulleys. A belt with 500 mm free length would have a maximum flex of 8 mm. (An approximate equivalent measurement would be a maximum flex of $\frac{1}{2}$ in on a free belt length of 33 in.)

A tractor engine fan belt should have a maximum flex, in one direction, of about 10 mm. This measurement will vary according to the

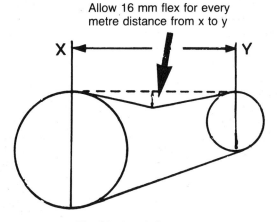

Fig. 85. Vee-belt tension

free length of the belt. Check with your operator's handbook for the belt tension for a particular machine.

Vee-belts are tensioned by adjusting one of the pulleys. Mechanically, the best drive arrangement consists of just two pulleys. One of the pulleys is carried by an adjustable bearing housing which is moved away from the second pulley to increase tension. An alternative method of belt adjustment is by fitting, or removing, spacing washers between the pulley flanges. This will alter the effective pulley diameter.

Other vee-belt drives have three or more pulleys. One of these is an idler pulley. It has a simple sliding adjustment used to keep the belt at the correct tension. An engine generator pulley is an example of an idler pulley used to tension a fan belt. Most idler pulleys, however, do nothing other than act as a belt tensioner.

Remember that a belt drive is reversed by crossing the belt. This arrangement must never be used as a means of tightening a slack belt.

Fitting Vee-belts

Careless fitting of vee-belts may damage both belt and pulley. Clean all traces of oil and grease from the flanges. Pulleys with damaged flanges (sides) must be replaced. Slacken the adjustment off completely before fitting the new belt. Resist the temptation to lever the belt over the flanges; this will lead to disaster when working with cast pulleys. Once fitted, set the belt at the correct tension. Check the adjustment after a fews hours' service because the belt will stretch during this period.

Correct pulley alignment is essential for long belt life. Place a straight edge across the faces of the pulley to check alignment. The sides of the flanges should just touch and be parallel with the straight edge. Adjust the position of the bearing housings if the alignment is wrong. Sometimes the pulleys will have flanges of different thickness. Allowance must be made for this when lining up the drive with a straight edge.

Vee-belt Sizes

There are standard sizes which apply to vee-belts. The dimensions are nominal because it would be impossible to manufacture belts to precise measurements. It is important to use the correct size of vee-belt in a vee pulley. There are several sizes of belt in common use, and the following table gives dimensions of those used on farm machines.

Table 24. Dimensions of vee-belts

Belt letter code	A	B	C	D
Cross-section size mm	13 × 8	17 × 11	22 × 14	32 × 19

Belt length is now given in millimetres and refers to the pitch length. Some manufacturers use the pitch length as the part number for a particular belt. For example, a belt with the number A950 is an A-section belt with a pitch length of 950 mm.

Vee-belts are meant to run dry. Sometimes they are dusted with French chalk, serving as a lubricant. Don't allow oil, grease or any type of belt dressing to come into contact with them. Oil and grease attacks rubber and seriously shortens the useful life of a vee-belt. Check the underside of belts for cracks and splits. This damage may go unnoticed for some while unless a thorough check is made.

OTHER TYPES OF BELT

Other belt drives used for farm equipment include flat, link vee, banded vee and toothed belts.

Flat belts are suitable for transmitting power over quite long distances. They are made from rubberised canvas, fabric or rubber. Canvas belts will benefit from an application of belt dressing. The flat belt may be endless (with no joins) or a jointed belt connected with an alligator type fastening or joining bolts. When a flat belt is cut in preparation for making a joint, it is vital to cut the ends off exactly square. A flat belt operates best on a pulley which has a slight crown, or dome, at the centre. The crown holds the belt in a central position on the pulley, even when it is running slightly out of alignment.

Link vee-belts are made up from rubberised canvas links held together with metal studs. This type of belt can be used where an endless belt cannot be fitted to the pulleys. Any number of links can be used, allowing a belt of any required length to be made. These belts run in normal vee-pulleys.

Toothed belts can be used as an alternative to a chain drive. They have a flat top surface with moulded teeth on the underside. These belts must be used with special pulleys which have the same tooth profile. This is the only type of belt suitable to drive components which are timed in relation to each other. A chain drive is normally used for this purpose.

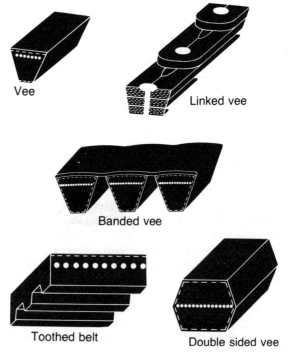

Vee

Linked vee

Banded vee

Toothed belt

Double sided vee

Fig. 86. Types of drive belt

A *banded vee-belt* is a combination of a flat belt and three or more vee-belts. The vee-belt sections are bonded to the flat upper part of the belt. They are used in purpose-made multiple vee-pulleys.

The *double vee-belt* is used for complicated drive arrangements where both sides of the belt are used on, for example, some combine harvester sieves and straw walkers.

Pulley Speeds

There is a relationship between the speed and diameter of a pair of belt pulleys. The size or speed of a pulley can be calculated with a simple formula. This can be useful when installing a drive for an implement modification or installing a new piece of workshop equipment. Use this formula:

$$\frac{\text{diameter of driving pulley (D)}}{\times \text{ rpm of driving pulley (D)}} = \frac{\text{diameter of driven pulley (F)}}{\times \text{ rpm of driven pulley (F)}}$$

Provided that the values are known for three of the four items in the formula, the unknown figure can be calculated.

Example: Find the speed of a 250 mm pulley driven by another pulley which has a diameter of 400 mm and runs at 1000 revolutions per minute.

$$\text{Speed of driven pulley (F)} = \frac{\text{diameter of } D \times \text{rpm of } D}{\text{diameter of } F}$$

$$= \frac{400 \times 1000}{250}$$

$$= 1600 \text{ rpm}$$

The same formula can be used to calculate the diameter of either pulley if both pulley speeds are known.

Note: The diameter used for calculating with vee-belt drives should be measured from the middle of the vee sides of the belt. This is called the Pitch Circle Diameter (PCD).

Changing Revolutions per Minute to Linear Speed

Speed in rpm can be converted to linear or peripheral speed with another simple formula. The peripheral speed relates to the speed of a point on the rim, or circumference, of a wheel. For example, the rasp bars on the cylinder of a combine harvester should run at approximately 1800 m/min (6000 ft/min) when threshing cereal crops. This speed is attained with a cylinder of 560 mm diameter running at 1000 rpm.

Use this formula to convert rpm to peripheral speed:

Peripheral speed (m/min) = circumference of wheel (m) × rpm
          OR   (ft/min) = circumference (ft) × rpm

Example: Find the speed (peripheral speed) of a belt driven by a 400 mm diameter pulley running at 500 rpm.

$$\text{Peripheral speed} = \text{diameter} \times 3 \cdot 142 \times \text{rpm}$$
$$= 0 \cdot 4 \text{ m} \times 3 \cdot 142 \times 500$$
$$= 628 \text{ m/min}$$

The same formula can be turned around to find the rpm of a driving pulley which will give the required peripheral or belt speed.

$$\text{Rpm of driving pulley} = \frac{\text{peripheral speed (m/min)}}{\text{circumference (m)}}$$

$$OR \qquad = \frac{\text{peripheral speed (ft/min)}}{\text{circumference (ft)}}.$$

The relationship between the speed of two gear wheels can be calculated with the same formula as that for pulley speeds and diameters. Before making the calculation, substitute pulley diameter for the number of teeth on each gear.

CHAIN DRIVES

There are two basic types of chain used for farm machinery. Long-pitch roller chain and malleable hook link chain are both used for low-speed power transmission. High-speed roller chain with much shorter links is used to drive fast-moving parts. Roller chain is made in simple (one row), duplex and triplex forms. The gear wheels used to support chain drives are called sprockets.

A roller chain consists of a number of connected links. The inner links have side plates, held together by two steel bushes which carry the rollers. The outer link plates are held together by steel pins which pass through the inner link bushes. The rollers run in contact with the sprocket teeth to give a smooth transmission of power. The rollers need lubrication, thin oil being better than thick.

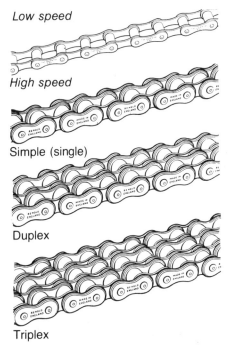

Low speed

High speed

Simple (single)

Duplex

Triplex

Fig. 87. Roller chains

Care of Roller Chains

Implement drive chains often suffer from neglect. At the end of a season's work all chain drives should be cleaned and lubricated. A chain which is partly seized through rust should be removed and soaked in oil. Chain drives on some machines provide a method of timing the operation of one part in relation to another, e.g. baler knotter drive. In such cases, make sure you know how to retime the drive before it is taken apart. The simple way is refer to the instruction manual. If one is not available, set the drive at a known point in its cycle then mark the sprockets and their housings with a centre punch. Make the marks in a way which ensures you cannot make a mistake during assembly. A roller chain has at least one joining link.

To get maximum service from a chain drive, it must have adequate lubrication, correct tension and the sprockets must be in line. A straight edge placed across the faces of the sprockets will show up any misalignment. Check that both sprocket faces are in line and exactly parallel. A fault here will cause rapid wear of the sprocket teeth and the

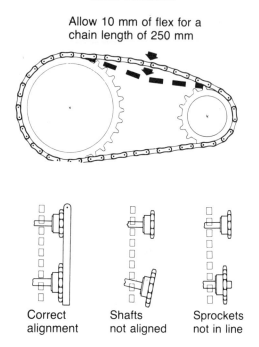

Fig. 88. Care of chain drives

chain. Tension is checked by measuring the amount of flex in the chain, midway between two sprockets. A rough guide to correct tension is to allow 10 mm of flex for every 250 mm of chain length between the two sprockets ($\frac{3}{8}$ in for every 10 in).

Chain Repairs

With continued use, chains will wear and on occasions break. There is a special extracting tool for removing links from a roller chain by separating the outer link from the inner link so that the chain can be opened out. It has two handles which open and close the jaws and a tee handle which operates the extractor screw. The handles are squeezed to open the jaws which are then placed over the outer plate. The jaws grip the plate when the handles are released. When the tee handle is turned, the outer plate is forced off the pin. Repeat the procedure for the second pin. The outer link can now be removed from the chain. Don't attempt to reuse the old outer link. The plates will be distorted and the old pin will make a weak joint.

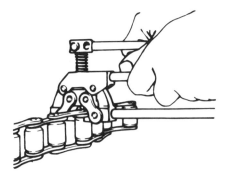

Fig. 89. Chain extractor

The simple way to reconnect a roller chain is with a special joining link. It has a spring clip which must be fitted with the split end of the clip trailing. As an alternative, a new link can be used. After it has been put together on the chain, use a rivet set to force the side plate close to the shoulders of the pins. Then lightly hammer over the ends of the pins until the side plate is secure.

Chain wear can be measured very easily. Place the opened chain on a flat piece of wood and drive a nail through the end link. Stretch the chain as far as you can and then measure its length. Compare this dimension with the original length which can be calculated by multiplying the number of links by the pitch measurement. The chain should be replaced if it has stretched by about 2 per cent beyond its original length. This amount of stretch is equal to an addition of 5 mm to a chain which was 250 mm when new. For a rough guide, maximum chain stretch should not exceed half a pitch.

It is recommended practice to replace the sprockets when a new chain is fitted. A new chain will have a high rate of wear on old sprockets.

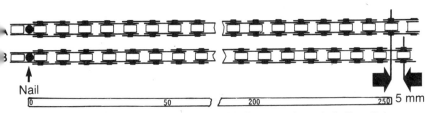

Maximum stretch 5 mm in 250 mm; this is approximately half a pitch

Fig. 90. Measuring chain wear

Altering the Length of a Chain

Roller chains can have links added or removed to alter their length. It is a simple matter to lengthen or shorten a chain by two links. Use a chain extractor to remove one outer and one inner link and then reconnect the chain. It is more likely that it will be necessary to shorten, or lengthen, a chain by one pitch (link).

A chain with an even number of links is shortened by one pitch if two links are removed with an extractor and a cranked, half link is used to connect the chain together (see fig. 91a).

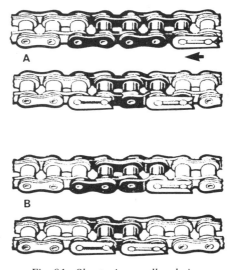

Fig. 91. Shortening a roller chain

A chain with an odd number of links will be one pitch shorter if the odd cranked link is removed and the chain is reconnected with a joining link (see fig. 91b).

Joining links for high-speed roller chains have an outer plate with grooved pins which take a spring-retaining clip. This clip holds the outer plate in position and must be fitted with the tails of the clip trailing.

Low-speed roller chains have a joining link which uses a long, thin split pin to hold the outer plate in position.

Chains in Dusty Conditions

Chain drives on machines where conditions are very dusty are sometimes protected by a chain case. This will normally have oil in it to provide lubrication. The oil level in the chain case needs a periodic check, and from time to time the oil should be changed. An adjustment for chain tension is normally provided and the tension must be checked at regular intervals.

Many chains which work in dusty conditions do not have this protection and it may be better to run such chains dry. Oil will collect dust and grit which makes a very abrasive paste. Chains which run dry will become shiny and will soon rust if left exposed to the weather, so at the end of the working season these chains should be washed down and then oiled. Take care to lubricate the pins and the rollers. Wipe off surplus oil.

It will pay to remove the chain occasionally, wash it in paraffin and soak it in oil. Surplus oil should be wiped off the chain before it is replaced.

Hook Link Chains

These are used for some slow-speed implement drives, especially where there is a risk of serious corrosion, for example, on a manure spreader floor conveyor. The links are hooked together and when the chain is fitted to the sprocket the hook must lead. The links may be cast or malleable steel. The chain can be taken apart without difficulty after the tension has been taken from the drive. The hook of a malleable link can be opened up slightly with a chisel if there is a problem when taking a chain apart. Chain tension is adjusted in the same way as for roller chains. An idler pulley, or sometimes a shaped wooden block, is used to set the tension.

OVERLOAD DEVICES

Chain and belt drives are often protected from damage through overloading by safety slip clutches. Where a drive system is timed, a slip clutch cannot be used, for example, on a pick-up baler knotter drive. In such cases, a safety shear bolt is used as an overload protection device.

Shear bolts are made from special steel and are meant to break at a certain load. Both the connected parts have a hard steel bush which takes the shearbolt, and these bushes must be replaced if they are loose, damaged or lost. Make sure that the shearbolt is tight before the drive is used and always use the correct shearbolt.

Safety Clutches

The serrated-face slip clutch, or clatter clutch, has two hard, serrated metal faces held together by a large compression spring. A castellated nut and securing split pin are used to set the spring tension. When

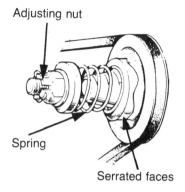

Adjusting nut

Spring

Serrated faces

Fig. 92. Serrated face slip clutch

overloading takes place, the drive pulley (see fig. 92) continues to turn but the driven shaft slows or stops. The movement of the faces against each other makes a loud clattering noise.

A friction plate slip clutch has smooth plates and is silent. The friction plates are held between smooth metal plates by spring pressure. In fig. 93 the power shaft is connected to the metal pressure plates. The friction plates are held between the pressure plates and the central disc which is secured to the output shaft. When overloading occurs, the power shaft

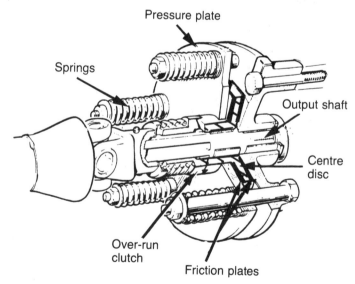

Pressure plate

Springs

Output shaft

Centre disc

Over-run clutch

Friction plates

Fig. 93. Friction plate slip clutch

continues to turn but the central plate and output shaft slow down or stop.

This type of slip clutch, illustrated on a power take-off drive is used in a very similar form to protect both belt and chain drives, especially on harvesting machinery.

An over-run clutch, used in power take-off drives also protects some chain drives, for instance, on a pick-up baler. It works in the same way as a bicycle freewheel with a spring-loaded drive mechanism which only drives in one direction. The over-run clutch will transmit power to the driven shaft but will not allow drive from the driven part to the input shaft. The over-run clutch in a baler flywheel makes a clicking sound as it slows down at its own pace after the power take-off has been disengaged. There is an over-run clutch in the pick-up cylinder drive on some balers.

Care of Safety Clutches

Serrated-face slip clutches need little attention. Check that the serrated faces are not seized together at the start of the season. Don't overtighten the spring and never allow it to become coil-bound (this is when the coils of the spring touch each other).

The friction plate slip clutch should be checked for operation at the start of the season; again, never allow the springs to become coil-bound. When it becomes necessary to set the springs in a coil-bound position to achieve a satisfactory drive, it is well past the time when the friction plates should have been replaced.

Consult the implement instruction book to find the correct setting for slip clutch springs. When no information is available, tighten the springs, a little at a time, until they are all coil-bound. Slacken the retaining nuts back for $1\frac{1}{2}$ to 2 turns. Check spring condition before assembling the clutch. Any spring which is short should be renewed.

Don't allow oil or grease to come into contact with the faces of the clutch plates. The faces should be clean, dry and free from all traces of corrosion.

Over-run clutches should be checked for free movement. Make sure that the spring-loaded pawls are not seized.

WIRING A SEVEN-PIN TRAILER PLUG

A seven-pin, or jack plug, is used for connecting trailer lights to a tractor or a road vehicle. The plug is usually made of a plastic material and is often damaged.

The outer cable contains seven separate wires, each with a different

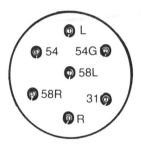

Fig. 94. Wiring a seven-pin plug

colour plastic insulation. The terminals on both plug and socket have an identification code which uses a combination of numbers and letters. Connections are made in the same way as any other electrical fitting. Care should be taken when stripping off the insulation material. Avoid any bare wire showing after the connection has been made.

Table 25 gives details of the wiring code for a seven-pin plug. Fig. 94 shows the relative position of the terminals when the plug is viewed from the socket end.

When fitting a seven-pin plug, use enough cable to ensure that it will not be stretched when the outfit turns a corner. Secure the cable in position with plenty of clips to prevent it from sagging or dragging along the ground.

Table 25. Wiring a seven-pin plug

Figure ref. no.	Plug marking code	Cable colour	Use of connection
1	L	yellow	nearside indicator light
2	54 G	blue	auxiliary lights or rear fog lamps
3	31	white	earth
4	R	green	offside indicator light
5	58 R	brown	offside rear light
6	54	red	stop lights
7	58 L	black	nearside rear light and number plate light

TYRES

Tyre life depends on the way the tyre is used and how well it is maintained. Storage of new tyres is important: keep them in a cool building, away from strong sunlight; don't keep oil or grease near tyres.

Skidding, low pressures and mechanical damage, such as scrubbing a trailer drawbar with the tread, will shorten the working life of a tyre. Make sure that the tyres are fitted the right way. A rear tractor tyre should have the 'V' pattern of the tread pointing upwards when viewed from behind the machine. Land wheel drive implements have the tread fitted in the opposite way.

Punctures

Tyre fitting and puncture repairs are done by the experts with great speed. They have the correct tools for this high-speed work, which may not be so in the farm workshop. Once the wheel is off the tractor or machine, tyre removal starts by releasing the air from the tube. The wheel should be placed flat on the floor. Put the valve core in a safe place for re-use.

The next task is to break the seal between the edge (bead) of the tyre and the wheel rim. Don't use a sledge hammer to do this work, such treatment will damage the tyre. There are various bead-breaking tools on the market. One type depends on leverage, another is a heavy tyre lever with a tube handle fitted over it. Hammer action with the tubular handle separates the bead from the rim. Once started, the tool is used to work right round the wheel until the bead is completely free. After the seal is broken on one side, turn the wheel over and repeat the process. Finally, use tyre levers, a set of three is best, to lever the tyre off.

The tube can now be removed and the puncture located. Put some air in the tube and then hold it under water. Watch for tell-tale air bubbles which show the position of the leak.

The puncture can be repaired with a patch and some rubber solution (adhesive) or with a vulcaniser. The latter applies the patch to the tube by a controlled heat process. In both cases, clean the area around the puncture and slightly roughen the surface before fixing the patch. Dust the area round the patch with some French chalk when the repair is complete.

Check the inside of the tyre for sharp objects which might have caused the puncture. If the tyre was removed completely, place it back on top of the rim which should be flat on the floor. Use French chalk or soapy water to lubricate the tyre bead. Make sure the tyre is the right way round. The tube can be put inside the tyre at this stage or when the lower bead has been fitted to the rim. Line up the valve with its locating hole in the rim. Once the lower bead is in place, locate the valve in its hole and secure it with the retaining nut. Apply French chalk to the upper bead and lever it into position. Take great care when using levers to make sure the tube is not nipped against the rim. Start work at a position opposite the valve and work round the rim in both directions. The tube can be seated on the rim by inflating it a little without fitting the valve core. It is better if the tyre is pushed onto the rim.

The tyre is now ready for inflation. This is a dangerous operation because the tyre could slip off the rim causing a serious injury. Stand well clear while inflating the tyre; don't sit on the tyre or allow anyone else to do so. The tyre can be stood upright for this work. Wheels with split rims must be inflated in a safety cage. Don't put more air into the tube than is necessary to seat the bead against the rim. Avoid pressure above 2 bar for a rear tyre on a tractor. If the bead will not seat at this pressure, release the air, check that the tyre is fitted correctly and inflate the tyre again. Set the tyre at the correct working pressure and refit the wheel.

The professional tyre fitter will often carry out a repair without removing the wheel from the tractor. This is not to be recommended for the farm workshop, especially for the mechanic who has little experience of the more conventional methods of doing tyre repairs.

ELECTRIC MOTORS

The maintenance of electric motors in the farm workshop is restricted to keeping them clean. A vacuum cleaner can be used to suck dirt from the cooling vents. Motors which have infrequent use should be run every two or three months—a few minutes' running will keep the bearings lubricated and prevent shaft seizure. Don't pile empty sacks, etc., on top of an electric motor. Take any steps possible to keep electric motors dry.

When a motor will not start, check the fuse. Provided that the power has been turned off, the terminal cover plate on the motor can be removed so that the terminals can be checked for tightness. If the motor hums but fails to turn, make sure that the drive belt can be turned by hand. Turn the motor off first. Apart from these simple checks, it is best to call in a qualified electrician to deal with electric motor problems. His services will certainly be needed if there is an unpleasant burning smell coming from the motor. This usually means that the motor has burnt out and needs to be replaced.

THINGS TO DO

1. Practise some of the methods suggested in this chapter for removing broken or seized bolts and studs. A scrapped machine will provide plenty of material.
2. Look for the different types of belt and chain drive mentioned in this chapter.
3. Check the tension of a vee-belt drive on a farm machine and set it to the correct adjustment if necessary.
4. Check a length of roller chain for wear. Find out how to shorten the chain by one pitch.
5. Dismantle a slip clutch and check the condition of the friction plates. Check with the implement instruction book to find the correct settings for the clutch springs.

QUESTIONS

1. How can an inexperienced mechanic find information about the correct assembly of a machine he is overhauling?
2. Why must a drive system using three vee-belts always have the belts replaced in complete sets?
3. Find the speed of a pulley which has a diameter of 300 mm. It is driven by a pulley 400 mm in diameter running at 450 rpm.
4. What is meant by the pitch of a chain link?
5. Give three factors which affect the working life of a tractor tyre.

Chapter 10

Tractor Repairs

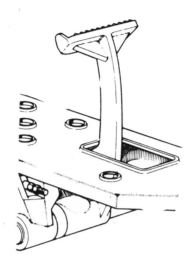

A NEW FARM tractor will be delivered complete with a comprehensive instruction book. It includes information about the maintenance of the engine, transmission, tyres, etc. Workshop manuals, available from many tractor dealers, provide full service information. These books can be rather expensive but are essential reading for the keen mechanic.

Information alone is not enough. Before attempting anything other than minor repairs, you will need some specialist tools and a good basic knowledge of tractor repairs. The complicated work, especially with hydraulics, transmission and fuel injection equipment, except for changing injectors, should be left to the expert. If you attempt this work without the correct tools and sufficient knowledge, the eventual cost can be far greater than it would be if the dealer's mechanic had been called in at the start. On the positive side, much can be done by the driver mechanic to keep farm tractors running economically and efficiently.

FUEL ECONOMY

Many tractors waste fuel. Savings can be made through careful maintenance and thoughtful use.

Clean Air

An engine uses vast amounts of air. Make sure that the air filter is clean. The oil bath should be cleaned out when there is about 12 mm ($\frac{1}{2}$ in) of dirt in it. Refill with clean oil to the level mark. Make sure that the gauze above the oil bath is clean too.

A dry air cleaner element is cleaned by removing it from the housing and knocking it gently against a tyre. Rotate the element between each tap. Don't bang the element against a hard surface, this will damage the filter. Make sure that the connections from the air cleaner to the inlet manifold are tight. Check the inside of the hoses for a build-up of dirt.

Watch for the warning signs. A restricted airflow due to a partly blocked air cleaner causes black smoke from the exhaust. The result is a waste of fuel. Many dry air cleaners have an indicator which warns the driver of restricted air flow to the engine. Check the air cleaner weekly, and when working in dusty conditions check daily.

Clean Fuel

Diesel engine fuel filters should be changed after about 600 hours. Check the instruction book for filter change period for your tractor. Turn off the fuel, remove and discard the old filter and fit a new element. Use new sealing rings. Don't wipe the parts of the filter with a fluffy rag. The fuel system must be bled after fitting a new filter. Use the lift pump priming lever if fitted, or gravity to remove the trapped air. Bleed from the filters first and then the injection pump.

Drain any water trapped in the fuel sediment bowl at weekly intervals. Fill tractor fuel tanks at night to reduce the build-up of water in the tank through condensation. Store the fuel properly and allow a new delivery to settle for at least 24 hours before it is used.

Plenty of Oil

Good lubrication is essential for top engine performance. Dirty oil and clogged filters bring heavy repair bills. The typical change period for diesel engine oil, and the filter, is 250 hours. Check the manual for change period for your tractor. Drain the oil from the engine when it is hot. Screw-in elements should be tightened by hand, not by a spanner. Use a new sealing ring.

The oil pressure gauge provides an indication of engine condition. Rapid loss of pressure when the engine reaches running temperature

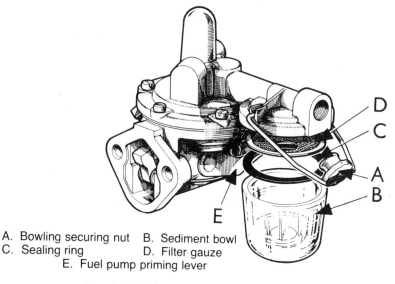

A. Bowling securing nut   B. Sediment bowl
C. Sealing ring   D. Filter gauze
        E. Fuel pump priming lever

Fig. 95. Diesel engine lift pump and sediment bowl

may be due to worn bearings, worn oil pump or thin oil. A blocked oil filter can cause high or low oil pressure depending on the position of the filter in relation to the gauge.

An engine has a crankcase breather to prevent a build-up of pressure in the crankcase, or sump. There is a filter in this breather. Check it periodically to make sure that it is not blocked.

INJECTORS

The performance of injectors should be checked after 600 hours' service; service agents have testers to carry this out. The fine holes in the nozzle of the injector wear and allow excess fuel into the injectors. Large quantities of black smoke from the exhaust can often be due to worn injectors.

Reconditioned injectors can be obtained from tractor dealers. It is well worth fitting a set of exchange injectors, especially when there is excessive black smoke and a loss of power. These symptoms can be expected by the time a set of injectors has completed 1000 hours. When buying exchange injectors, get some new injector sealing washers too.

Clean all the dirt from around the area of the injectors, remove the leak-off pipes and injector pipes. Protect the exposed pipes to keep dirt

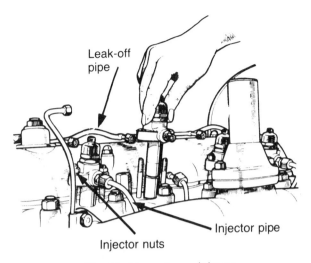

Leak-off pipe

Injector pipe

Injector nuts

Fig. 96. Removing an injector

out. Finally, take off the injector retaining nuts and remove the injectors. It may be necessary to use leverage to withdraw the injector because of a carbon build-up around the nozzle. Take care with the lever as damage to adjacent parts must be avoided.

Wipe out the injector hole and make sure that the old injector washer has come out with the injector. Put the new sealing washers on the replacement injectors. A spot of grease will help to keep them in place. Fit the injectors and tighten them down evenly to keep them square in their holes. Don't overtighten the nuts. The injector and leak-off pipes can now be refitted.

COOLING

Engines waste fuel if they overheat or run cold. Make sure that the fan belt is tensioned correctly; the radiator should be clean and the water level checked frequently. The thermostat, fitted at the front of the cylinder head, controls water flow through the cooling system. Failure to warm up quickly or repeated overheating can be caused by a faulty thermostat. This can be checked for operation by removing it from its housing and dipping it in hot water. The thermostat should open when hot and close when left to cool. Some thermostats have the temperature at which they start to open marked on them. A thermostat which is seized in the open position when it is removed from a cool engine is faulty. Test closed thermostats with hot water. Check the condition of the sealing washer in the radiator pressure cap and renew it if necessary.

WHEELS AND BRAKES

Correct *tyre pressures* are important, both for long tyre life and for efficient grip. The actual pressure for a tyre will depend on its size, whether it is a radial or cross-ply tyre and on the maximum load it is expected to carry. Refer to the tractor instruction book for correct settings. You may find the pressure stated in pounds per square inch (psi), or kilogrammes per square centimetre (kg/cm^2), or bar. Psi is familiar to everyone but the other units of pressure may be a puzzle. 1 bar is atmospheric pressure and is equivalent to 14·7 psi. A tyre pressure of 1·7 bar is equivalent to 25 psi. 1 kg/cm^2 is about equal to 1 bar.

The basic rules for tyre pressures are to increase the pressure by about 0·2 bar above the normal land work setting when the tractor does a lot of road work. Front tyres should be at least 6 ply and have a pressure of up to 1 bar above land work setting when used with a front-mounted loader.

Brakes which are set too tight will cause the linings, or discs, to bind and waste fuel. Drum brakes need equal adjustment on both wheels. The pedals must be balanced so that when they are locked together, the tractor pulls up square when the brakes are applied. If the tractor pulls to one side, the pedals are out of balance and the fault must be rectified by adjusting the length of one brake rod. Each rod connects its pedal to the brake assembly and has an adjustable connector, usually at the pedal end. The connector is held on to the pedal by a clevis pin, secured with a split pin. It is usual for the pedal with the greatest movement to be adjusted.

Remove the connector from the brake pedal and lengthen the brake rod as necessary. This should bring both pedals to the same height when equal pressure is applied to them. This check is made with the pedals unlatched. An alternative test for pedal balance is to lock the brakes together and drive the tractor forward at a steady speed. Apply the brakes with the power still on. The tractor will pull up square if the pedals are correctly balanced.

Disc brakes are usually adjusted and balanced in one operation. The pedal position is altered with an adjusting nut on the brake assembly. The aim is to set both pedals at the same height above the cab floor. This measurement varies with different tractors, so check with the instruction book.

Only unlatch the pedals when the use of the independent brakes is necessary.

ADDING WEIGHT: WATER BALLAST

Wheel grip is improved by adding weight. This will improve fuel economy in most conditions. Added weight can waste fuel and cause soil compaction when working on land where extra weight is unnecessary. Cast-iron weights allow quick fitting or removal. Water ballast does not have this advantage.

1 litre of water weighs 1 kilogramme; 1 gallon weighs 10 pounds. It is usual to water ballast a tractor tyre to 75 per cent of its capacity. A 13·6/12–38 tyre with 75 per cent water ballast will have an added weight of 190 kg (420 lb).

Calcium chloride is added at a rate of 1 kg per 5 litres to protect the water from frost. This solution must not be used for engine cooling systems. This will give a total added weight of about 275 kg to each wheel.

Before ballasting a wheel, it must be jacked clear of the ground and the rear axle of the tractor supported with stands. Chock the front wheels to stop the tractor moving accidentally. Set the valve core at the highest point, release the air and remove the core. Check in the instruction book to find how much water is needed for the tractor wheels.

Put about one-quarter of the required water in a plastic container. Add the chemical and stir until it has dissolved completely. Then add the remainder of the water. The chemical must always be added to the water—not the water to the chemical. The mixing process will heat the water. Allow it to cool before attempting to ballast the tyre.

Fit a special adaptor valve to the tube after the valve core is removed. Connect the adaptor to the container with a suitable hose if gravity filling. A pump can be used to force the ballast into the tube. Release trapped air from the tube from time to time during filling; the filling adaptor has a release valve for this purpose. When the water reaches the level of the valve, filling should stop. The adaptor is removed and the valve core replaced. Turn the valve to the lowest point and inflate the tyre to its normal pressure. Use a proper air/water pressure gauge; a normal dry-air gauge will be ruined if used on a ballasted tyre.

To remove water ballast first jack up the tractor and put axle stands in place. Remove the valve core and allow the water to run out. It can be collected for reuse if desired. Draining is carried out with the valve at the bottom but some water will be left in. The drained water should be stored in a plastic container with a label to show its contents.

Any water ballast solution which has splashed on to surrounding metal parts or your skin must be removed. The chemical will corrode the metal and burn your skin.

THE CLUTCH

The clutch pedal must have some free movement before the pressure of the clutch springs is felt. This is called clutch pedal free play. It is checked by pushing the clutch pedal down with the hand and noting the distance it travels before resistance is felt. The measurement will vary from 12 to 38 mm ($\frac{1}{2}$ to $1\frac{1}{2}$ in). Adjustment is made by altering the length of the rod connecting the pedal to the clutch control lever. Sometimes the pedal is moved on its shaft. Here again, it is important to check with the instruction book to find the correct setting.

Too much free play makes gear engagement difficult. Too little will cause excessive clutch thrust bearing wear and the clutch may slip.

SETTING VALVE TAPPETS

Engine valves are opened by the pushrods and rocker arms. They are closed by the valve springs. A gap, or clearance, is left between the face of the rocker arm and the end of the valve stem. This is called the tappet clearance. There is a correct setting for the tappet clearance on every engine which is given in the instruction book. An example of clearances is 0·40 mm (0·015 in) for the inlet valve and 0·47 mm (0·018 in) for the exhaust valves. Some engines have much smaller clearances. The valves may not close properly when the engine is hot if the setting is too small. A wide clearance will open the valves late and there will be a tapping noise from the engine.

Tappet clearance is checked with a feeler gauge. Adjustment is made with spanners or a spanner and screwdriver. The clearance must be checked when the valve is closed.

The 'nine rule' can be used to set the valve in the correct position for setting the tappets when working on a four-cylinder engine. The valve at the front, near the fan, is No. 1 and the back valve is No. 8. With the injectors removed, the engine can be turned over by means of the fan belt (set tight) or with a spanner on the crank pulley nut. To set the engine ready for adjusting No. 1 valve tappet clearance, turn the engine until No. 8 valve is open. The nine rule is used by subtracting the number of the open valve (8) from 9 which makes valve 1 ready for adjustment. When valve 6 is open, valve 3 is in the correct position and so on.

The method of adjusting tappets is shown in fig. 97. With the feeler gauge in position, the locking nut is slackened and the adjusting screw is turned slightly until the blade of the feeler gauge is a close fit. The blade must not be so tight that it is difficult to remove. Tighten the lock nut and recheck the adjustment.

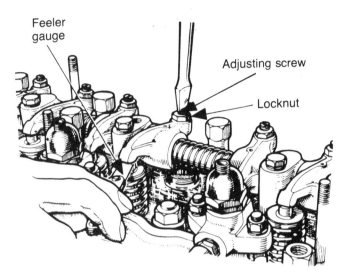

Fig. 97. Setting valve tappets

Another way of setting the valves in position for tappet adjustment is to turn the engine until the piston of the chosen cylinder is at top dead centre (TDC) on the compression stroke. Both valves will be closed and the tappets can be adjusted. This method can be used to check the tappets for each cylinder of a multi-cylinder engine.

MISFIRING

A multi-cylinder engine sometimes misfires on one cylinder. There are many causes including stuck or burnt valves, broken piston rings, leaking gasket, faulty injector or sparking plug.

Misfiring can be located with a simple check. Slacken off each injector pipe in turn and listen to the engine note. When the injector pipe to a working cylinder is slackened, the misfire will be even worse. Retighten the pipe and the engine will pick up again. When the injector pipe to the faulty cylinder is loosened, there will be no change in engine note. Take care when slackening the pipes as fuel will spray from the unions at high pressure.

A spark ignition engine is checked in a similar way. Use a screwdriver with an insulated handle to short out each sparking plug in turn. Listen to the engine note.

Spark Ignition Fault Finding

Use the following checks to find where current is lost in a spark ignition system.

- Check the battery condition, use a hydrometer (see fig. 30) or operate the starter motor. If it turns at normal speed, move to the next check. The battery may be in good condition but the terminals might be loose or corroded.
- With the aid of a simple test lamp—a 12 volt bulb with a wire to each terminal—check for current flow at the SW terminal on the coil. Touch one test lamp wire on the SW terminal and the other to earth. If current flows, the bulb will light up. If there is no light, suspect a faulty switch, loose terminals or a broken wire.
- Check the terminal marked CB with the test lamp. The bulb should light up when the contact breaker points are flicked open. If the bulb does not light, suspect a faulty low-voltage circuit in the coil.
- The contact breaker points must be clean, free from oil and set at the correct gap. The test lamp proves they are working if it is connected to the CB terminal on the coil and to earth. The light should go out when the points are closed.
- Check the condenser and high-voltage side of the coil by removing the high-voltage lead from the centre of the distributor cap. Leave it connected to the coil. Hold the end of the lead about 5 mm from the engine block and flick the contact breaker points with an insulated screwdriver. A spark should jump from the lead to the block. If there is no spark, suspect the high-voltage side of the coil or the condenser.
- Fit a replacement condenser and repeat the above check. If there is still no spark, change the coil.
- With the high-voltage lead in the coil, hold the other end about 5 mm from the metal part of the rotor arm. If the insulation on the rotor arm is cracked, a spark will be seen. If this happens fit a new rotor arm.
- Check the distributor cap for cracks. Make sure that the carbon brush at the centre of the cap is in good condition and free to move. Check plug leads too. They may be faulty, the terminals may be corroded or loose.
- A spark plug can only be checked by using a proper tester. The plug will work when placed on the cylinder head and the engine is turned but the spark may break down when exposed to the working pressure of the cylinder. If in doubt, fit new plugs.

STARTING PROBLEMS

The battery is a major culprit when starting problems occur. Keep it well charged, especially in winter, and make sure the terminals are clean and tight. Check the earth strap connection from the battery to the engine.

Check that the solenoid connections are tight. When there is no obvious fault, the solenoid or starter motor probably needs replacing. This can be done in the farm workshop but remember to disconnect the battery before starting work. Service exchange starters are readily available.

Another problem can arise through a faulty cold-start heater. It can be removed and bench-tested for operation by connecting it to a battery.

Charging System

Make sure that the fan belt is tensioned correctly. The generator cannot work properly if the drive belt is slipping.

Check that the terminals are clean and tight. A simple fault, such as a loose terminal, is often the cause of a low charging rate or complete loss of charge.

A service exchange alternator or dynamo can be obtained and can be fitted without difficulty in the workshop.

THINGS TO DO

1. Find out how often the engine oil and the fuel filter element should be changed on the tractors at your farm.
2. Keep the clutch pedal free play on your tractor adjusted correctly. Check with the tractor instruction book for the setting.
3. Check the tappet adjustment on a multi-cylinder engine.
4. Practise the procedure outlined in this chapter for tracing a fault in a coil ignition system.
5. Keep the battery terminals and earth strap connections on your tractor in good condition. They should be clean and tight.

QUESTIONS

1. Describe a method for locating a misfiring cylinder on a diesel engine.
2. How should calcium chloride, used for water ballasting a tyre, be mixed with the water?
3. How should the tyre pressure of a water-ballasted tyre be checked?
4. What is the 'nine rule'?
5. State the checks which can be made to find a fault in a tractor starting system.

Table 26. Metric conversion tables

BRITISH TO METRIC

METRIC TO BRITISH

LENGTH

1 inch (in)	= 2·54 cm	1 millimetre (mm)	= 0·0394 in
	or 25·4 mm	1 centimetre (cm)	= 0·394 in
1 foot (ft)	= 0·30 m	1 metre (m)	= 1·09 yd
1 yard (yd)	= 0·91 m	1 kilometre (km)	= 0·621 miles
1 mile	= 1·61 km		

Conversion Factors

inches to cm	× 2·54		
or mm	× 25·4	centimetres to in	× 0·394
feet to m	× 0·305	millimetres to in	× 0·0394
yards to m	× 0·914	metres to ft	× 3·29
miles to km	× 1·61	metres to yd	× 1·09
		kilometres to miles	× 0·621

AREA

1 sq inch (in^2)	= 6·45 cm^2	1 sq centimetre (cm^2)	= 0·16 in^2
1 sq foot (ft^2)	= 0·093 m^2	1 sq metre (m^2)	= 1·20 yd^2
1 sq yard (yd^2)	= 0·836 m^2	1 sq metre (m^2)	= 10·8 ft^2
1 acre (ac)	= 4047 m^2	1 hectare (ha)	= 2·47 ac
	or 0·405 ha		

Conversion Factors

sq feet to m^2	× 0·093	sq metres to ft^2	×10·8
sq yards to m^2	× 0·836	sq metres to yd^2	× 1·20
acres to ha	× 0·405	hectares to ac	× 2·47

VOLUME (LIQUID)

1 fluid ounce (1 fl oz)		100 millilitres (ml or cc)	= 0·176 pints
(0·05 pint)	= 28·4 ml	1 litre	= 1·76 pints
1 pint	= 0·568 litres	1 kilolitre (1000 litres)	= 220 gal
1 gallon (gal)	= 4·55 litres		

Conversion Factors

pints to litres	× 0·568	litres to pints	× 1·76
gallons to litres	× 4·55	litres to gallons	× 0·220

WEIGHT

1 ounce (oz)	= 28·3 g	1 gram (g)	= 0·053 oz
1 pound (lb)	= 454 g	100 grams	= 3·53 oz
	or 0·454 kg	1 kilogram (kg)	= 2·20 lb
1 hundredweight (cwt)	= 50·8 kg	1 tonne (t)	= 2204 lb
1 ton	= 1016 kg		or 0·984 ton
	or 1·016 t		

Conversion Factors

ounces to g	× 28·3	grams to oz	× 0·0353
pounds to g	× 454	grams to lb	× 0·00220
pounds to kg	× 0·454	kilograms to lb	× 2·20
hundredweights to kg	× 50·8	kilograms to cwt	× 0·020
hundredweights to t	× 0·0508	tonnes to tons	× 0·984
tons to kg	× 1016·0		
tons to tonnes	× 1·016		

Additional Reading

The following list of publications will be useful to the reader who wishes to gain further knowledge on the topics covered in this book.

Farm Machinery by Brian Bell, published by Farming Press Ltd.

Farm Electric Handbooks and *Safe Use of Electricity on the Farm and in Horticulture.* A series of booklets published by the Electricity Council, Farm-Electric Centre, National Agricultural Centre, Kenilworth, Warwickshire CV8 2LS.

Agricultural Safety Leaflets. A range of leaflets which deal with all aspects of farm safety including Workplaces, Field Machinery Regulations and First Aid. Available from the Health and Safety Executive, Eagle House, Cannon St, London EC4 6HT and from regional offices.

Abrasive Wheels: Safety in installation and use, SHW 264. A leaflet published by the Health and Safety Executive.

Farm Water Supply. A set of five leaflets published by the Ministry of Agriculture, Fisheries and Food, Tolcarno Drive, Pinner, Middlesex HA5 2DT.

BOC Handbook of Operating Instructions for Gas Cutting and Welding.
BOC Safe under Pressure.
BOC Murex Manual Arc Welding Application Guide.
Three booklets available from Regional Offices of BOC Ltd.

In addition, the reader can find much useful information from catalogues and instruction sheets published by manufacturers of hand tools, power tools and workshop equipment.

Tractor and machinery manufacturers produce workshop manuals for much of their equipment. These manuals are usually available either from local dealers or the makers of the equipment. There is normally a charge for the publications.

Index

Abrasive sheets, 143
Abrasive wheel dresser, 68
— —, Regulations, 66
— —, types, 68
Adhesives for gaskets, 95
— —, threads, 90
Adjustable spanner, 26
Aerosol sprays, 151
Air cleaner, 207
—, line, 72
A/F spanners, 29
Alkathene pipe, 163
Allen keys, 26
Alloys, 100
Alloy steel, 103
Aluminium, 109
—, bronze, 109
—, oxide paper, 144
American National threads, 86
Angle grinder, 64
Annealing copper, 108
—, steel, 105
Anvil, 175
Arc welding, 127
Automatic drinker, 168
— —, water level adjustment, 167
Axle stand, 75

Babbit metal, 109
Bakelite, 111
Ball bearings, 187
—, pein hammer, 32
—, valve, 156, 166
— —, washer replacement, 167
Banded vee-belt, 193
Banjo pipe union, 98
BA threads, 82, 86
Battery charger, 72
—, testing, 73
Bearing assembly, 187
—, removal, 185
—, race removal, 186
Bench grinder, 65
Bending sheet metal, 179
Belts, 189

Benches, 15
Bevel, 61
Bib tap, 164
Bifurcated rivet, 91
Bleeding fuel systems, 207
Blowpipe, 116
Blowtorch, 108, 146, 159, 162
Bolt cutters, 51
—, heads, 83
—, threading, 52
—, types, 28
Bolster, 39
Box spanner, 26
Brake pedal adjustment, 210
Brass, 108
Broken bolt removal, 182
Bronze, 109
—, welding, 123
BSF, 86
BSP, 86, 158
BSW, 86
Burst water pipes, 176
Bush fitting, 186
—, removal, 185
Butt joint, 121, 133

Cabinetmaker's screwdriver, 30
Calcium chloride, 211
Calipers, 58, 187
Capillary joint, 159
Carbon, 100
—, arc welder, 138
—, steels, 103
Carburising, 106
Carburising flame, 119, 123
Carriage bolt, 82
Case hardening, 106
Cast iron, 101
— —, welding, 126, 136
Castellated nut, 84, 90
Causes of corrosion, 141
Cellulose paint, 148
Centre punch, 38
Chain drive alignment, 196
— —, joining links, 198

— —, link extractor, 197
— —, measurement of wear, 197
— —, tension, 196
Charging system, 215
Chilled cast iron, 101
Chisel, cold, 38
— —, safety in use, 40
— —, sharpening, 39
— —, uses, 41
Circlip, 95, 187
—, pliers, 36
Claw hammer, 32
Cleaning damaged threads, 85
Club hammer, 32
Clutch pedal adjustment, 212
Coil bound, 201
Combination pliers, 32
—, spanner, 26
Compressor, 72, 150
Compression joint, 159, 163
Copper, 94, 108
—, pipe, 159
— —, sizes, 162
—, washers, 95
Cork gaskets, 95
Corrosion prevention, 146
Cotter pins, 92
Crane, 75
Crankcase breather, 208
Creosote, 151
Cross pein hammer, 32
Crosspoint screwdriver, 30

Die nut, 52
—, stock, 158
Dies, types, 53
—, use, 53, 87, 158
Diesel fuel filters, 207
— —, injectors, 208
— —, lift pump, 208
— —, storage, 18
Distilled water, 72
Dividers, 58
De-watering fluid, 147
Dome nut, 85
Doorways, 14
Downhand welding, 133
Drawfiling, 46
Drill accessories, 62
—, bits, 64, 96
—, bit sharpening, 65

—, electric, 62
— —, selection of, 62
— —, use, 63
Drilling, lubricants for, 64
—, out broken studs, 184
—, sheet metal, 180
Duckboards, 15
Duplex chain, 195
Duralumin, 110

Electric arc welding of cast iron, 136
— — —, downhand technique, 133
— — —, equipment, 128
— — —, eye protection, 129
— — —, protective clothing, 129
— — —, striking an arc, 131
— — —, weaving technique, 133
Electric drills, 62
—, motor maintenance, 204
—, shock, 21
Electrician's pliers, 35
—, screwdriver, 30
Electrodes for cutting, 138
— —, welding, 130
—, storage of, 130
Electrolyte, 72
Emery cloth, 143
End cutting pliers, 36
Engine cooling system, 209
—, oil change, 207
—, starting troubles, 214
Engineer's hammer, 32
—, pliers, 34
—, screwdriver, 30
Extension cable, 71
External calipers, 57
Extinguishers, 23
Extracting broken studs, 183
Exhaust fumes, 22

Feather key, 29
Feeler gauge, 57, 212
Ferrous metals, 100
Fibre glass, 111
—, washers, 95
File card, 47
Files, types, 42
— —, use, 45
Fillet weld, 121, 134
Fire extinguisher, 23
First aid, 24

Flame cleaning, 146
Flashback arrester, 116
Flat belts, 191
—, file, 44
—, washer, 94
Flux, 114, 121, 128, 162
Folded edge joint, 179
Forgework, 175
Forging an eye, 176
French chalk, 203
Friction plate slip clutch, 200
Fuel storage, 18
—, pipe unions, 97

Galvanised steel, 103, 109
Garnet paper, 144
Gasket paper, 95
Gasket materials, 94
Gas thread, 86
Gate valve, 164
Gear speeds, 194
Gib head key, 93
Glasspaper, 144
Goggles, 67, 118
Grease, 19, 95
—, gun, 78
—, nipples, 96
Grey cast iron, 101
Grinders, bench, 65
— —, portable, 69
— —, safe use, 67
Grub screw, 82
Guillotine, 71
Gunmetal, 67

Hacksaws, blades, 47, 70
—, hand, 47, 155
—, power, 70
—, types, 47
—, use, 48
Hammers, types, 32
—, use, 33
Hand drill, 49
—, file, 44
Hardening steel, 104
Hard surfacing, 123, 136
Hexagon bolts, 82
High tensile bolts, 87
Hole saw, 156
Hook link chain, 199
Hub puller, 78

Hydraulic jack, 74
Hydrometer, 73

Inspection lamp, 16
Internal calipers, 58
Iron, 100

Jacks, 22, 74
Joints, copper pipe, 162
—, polythene pipe, 163
—, steel pipe, 157

Keys, types, 92
—, removal, 93
Knife section replacement, 175
Knotting solution, 153

Lagging water pipes, 170
Lap joint, 121, 179
Lead, 110
Ledger plate, 189
Leftward welding, 122
Leg vice, 76
Letter punches, 61
Lifting tackle, 74
Linked vee-belt, 192
Linear speed, 193
Locking devices for nuts, 88
—, plate, 89
—, wire, 90
Lock nuts, 84, 90
London screwdriver, 31
Low carbon steel, 102
Lubrication equipment, 78
Lubricants for drilling, 64
—, storage of, 19

Machine screws, 82
Malleable castings, 102
—, link chain, 194
Measuring tools, 56
Metalwork vice, 76
Micrometer, care and use, 61
—, Imperial measurement, 59
—, Internal, 60
Micrometer, metric measurement, 58
—, readings, 59
Mild steel, 102
Misfiring, 213
Multiple vee-belts, 189

Nails, 96
Neutral flame, 119
Nickel, 104
Nine rule, 212
Nipple drinker, 168
Nuts, 84
—, removal of seized, 182
Nylon, 111

Oilcan, 78
Oil pressure gauge, 207
Olive, 98, 114, 160
Open end spanners, 25
Ordering spares, 97
'O' rings, 188
Overload devices, 199
Over run clutch, 201
Oxy-acetylene cutting blowpipe, 125
— — —, gas pressures, 126
— — —, nozzle maintenance, 126
— — —, techniques, 125
— —, welding, edge preparation, 120
— — —, equipment, 116
— — —, flame setting, 119
— — —, fluxes, 121
Oxy-acetylene welding nozzle maintenance, 124
— — — —, reamers, 124
— — — —, selection, 118
— — —, problems, 138
— — —, protective clothing, 118
— — —, rods, 121
— — —, safety precautions, 127
— — —, techniques, 122
— — —, types of joint, 121
Oxidation, 114, 121, 128
Oxidising flame, 119

Paint, 148
—, brushes, 149
—, remover, 147
—, spraying, 150
Painting, 147
Paper gaskets, 94
Paraffin, 64
Pedestal drill, 62
Pedestal grinder, 65
Peripheral speed, 193
Personal safety, 22
Phillips screwdriver, 30

Phosphor bronze, 109
Pig iron, 101
Pillar tap, 164
Pilot hole, 63, 157, 184
Pin hammer, 32
—, punch, 38
Pins, types, 94
Pipe bending, 157
Pipe bending spring, 157
—, couplings, 171
—, cutter, 155
—, dies, 158
—, fittings, 159
—, thread, 86
—, vice, 154
Pipework, installation of, 169
—, frost protection, 170
—, through walls, 169
Pitch circle diameter, 193
Plastics, 110
Pliers, types, 34
—, use, 37
Plug tap, 52
Polythene, 111
—, pipe, 162
Polystyrene, 111, 170
Pop rivets, 92, 174
Portable grinder, 69
Positional welding, 123, 135
Power hacksaw, 70
—, take-off shaft repair, 187
—, tools, types, 62
— —, safe use, 20
Preheating, 137
Pressure regulator, 116
—, washer, 145
Primer paint, 148
PTFE tape, 111, 160, 163, 172
Puller, 77
Pulley alignment, 191
—, blocks, 75
—, speeds, 193
—, types, 189, 192
Punch, 36, 91
Puncture repair, 203
PVC, 111, 163

Rasp, 45
Reamer, 56
Reaper file, 45
Red oxide paint, 148

222

Rightward welding, 122
Rivet set, 38
—, snap, 38
—, types, 91
Riveting technique, 173
—, knife sections, 175
Roller chain, 194
—, type pipe cutter, 155
Roll pins, 94
Round file, 45
Rubber, 111
Rule, 56
Rust, 103
—, prevention, 146
—, preventative solutions, 147

Safe edge file, 43
Safety, 19
Screwdrivers, 30
Screwdriver sizes, 31
—, sharpening, 31
—, use, 32
Screw jack, 74
Screws, 96
Scriber, 61, 176
Seals, 94, 188
Seized nuts, 182
Self locking nuts, 85
— —, wrench, 35, 36
—, tapping screws, 83, 180
Serrated face slip clutch, 199
—, shaft, 93
Service exchange injectors, 209
Set screws, 82
Seven-pin plug, 201
Shafts, splined, 93
—, serrated, 93
Shakeproof washer, 89
Sharpening mower knives, 189
Shear bolts, 87, 199
Shearing machine, 71
Sheet metal work, 178
Side cutting pliers, 35
Silicon carbide abrasive, 68, 143, 144
Sledge hammer, 32
Slings, 75
Slip clutch types, 199
— —, adjustment, 201
Snifting, 116
Socket spanners, 26
Soft faced hammer, 32

—, vice jaws, 77
Solder, 110, 114, 159
Soldering iron, 113
—, technique, 114
Spanners, 25
—, sizes, 29
—, safe use of, 29
Spark ignition fault finding, 214
—, patterns when grinding metal, 107
Specific gravity, 73
Splined shaft, 93
Split pins, 94
Spray gun, 150
—, painting, 150
Spring calipers, 57
—, washers, 89
Sprocket, 194
Square, 61
—, file, 45
Stainless steel, 104
Starting problems, 214
Steam cleaner, 146
Steel, 102
—, identification of, 106
—, wool, 159
Step welding, 137
Stillsons, 154
Stop tap, 164
Stores, 17
Straight edge, 61, 196
Straightening components, 176
Stud, 83
—, extractor, 184
—, removal, 83, 183
SWG, 96
Synthetic enamel paint, 148

Tab washer, 89
Tank cutter, 156
Taper punch, 38, 176
—, roller bearing, 187
Tappet adjustment, 212
Tap gland packing, 164
—, for cutting threads, 52, 159
—, washers, 164
—, for water, 164
Tapping drill sizes, 54
Temper colours, 105
Tempering steel, 105
Thawing frozen pipes, 170

Thinners, 148, 150
Thread charts, 88
—, form, 86
—, gauge, 87
—, identification, 87
—, pitch, 86
—, types, 85
Three square file, 45
Timber, 111
Tin, 109
—, plate, 103, 109
Tinning, 114
Tinsnips, 49
Toothed vee-belt, 192
Torque wrench, 27
Trickle charger, 72
Triplex chain, 195
Trolley jack, 74
Try square, 61
Tungsten carbide discs, 144
Turpentine substitute, 147
Twist drill, 64
— —, sharpening, 65
Tyre, 203
—, bead breaking, 207
—, levers, 207
—, pressure, 210
— —, gauge, 211

UNC, 88
UNF, 88
Universal joint repair, 187

Valve tappet setting, 212
Vee belts, 189
— —, adjustment, 190
— —, fitting, 191

— —, sizes, 191
Vices, 75
—, fitting to bench, 76
—, for water pipe, 154
—, grips, 77, 154

Washers, 89, 94
Water ballasting tyres, 211
Water pipe, copper, 159
— —, fittings, 161
— —, polythene, 163
— —, PVC, 163
— —, steel, 157
— —, vice, 154
Welding, 115
—, bay, 15
White cast iron, 101
—, spirit, 147
Wing nut, 84
Wire, 90, 96
—, brushes, 143
Wired edge, 179
Wiring a trailer plug, 202
Wood preservatives, 151
—, screws, 96
— —, sizes of, 96
Woodruff key, 92
Work hardening, 108
Workshop building, 14
—, heating, 16
—, lighting, 16
—, safety, 19
—, site, 14
—, ventilation, 16
Wrought iron, 102

Zinc, 103, 109